ENGINEERING MECHANICS

ENGINEERING MECHANICS

BY

SEIBERT FAIRMAN
Professor of Applied Mechanics, Purdue University

AND

CHESTER S. CUTSHALL
Professor of Applied Mechanics, Purdue University

NEW YORK

JOHN WILEY & SONS, Inc.

LONDON: CHAPMAN & HALL, LIMITED

PREFACE

In view of the fact that several good textbooks are already available in the field of elementary engineering mechanics, the authors realize that some explanation may be due for introducing a new volume on this subject. Books in this field differ from one another principally in the amount of material covered, the arrangement, and the manner of presentation. It is intended that this book shall differ from others in one or more of these aspects.

The time available for a basic course in mechanics in many institutions is limited by other curricular requirements. Therefore, instead of planning a comprehensive treatise on the subject, the authors have attempted to plan a textbook which can be covered in the time usually allotted to the subject without the necessity of omitting large sections, thus destroying the continuity. To accomplish this purpose, it is necessary to avoid much repetition of topics previously covered in prerequisite courses, and to eliminate topics which may properly be deferred to more advanced courses. Accordingly, proofs of certain propositions such as the parallelogram law and Varignon's theorem, usually demonstrated in the general physics course, are here omitted. Likewise, topics such as product of inertia which may properly be considered in advanced strength of materials, certain parts of kinematics, and balancing of reciprocating parts of mechanisms are also omitted. Other topics are included, particularly in kinetics, which may conveniently be omitted if time limitations make it necessary. In recognition of the growing importance of dimensional analysis and its applications, a very brief introduction to this subject has been made at the beginning of that part of the book dealing with kinetics, and the dimensional formula is given for each new quantity taken up thereafter.

In arranging the material, the authors were guided by the belief that a task may be accomplished with greater facility if all the necessary tools are available at the beginning. Hence, the various processes for resolving forces into components, combining into resultants, and determining moments are explained for all types of force systems before entering into the discussion of static equilibrium. In kinetics, the relations between work and kinetic energy are developed at an early point so as to be available for use in the dynamics of rotating bodies.

In the presentation of the material, the authors have endeavored to avoid making the subject appear more complex than necessary. A knowledge of integral calculus is assumed, and this branch of mathematics is employed as the occasion requires; however, the use of calculus is not indicated when simple algebra is sufficient. A liberal number of solved examples are supplied to illustrate and explain further the topics under discussion and to arouse the student's interest. These are followed by numerous problems for the student to solve. The answers are given for all such problems because the authors feel that the student acquires a greater confidence in his progress if he has a check on his results. Most of the answers have been determined by slide-rule computation to the nearest third significant digit. Instructors who prefer that answers not be given may make changes in the data. Although the authors have endeavored to furnish problems of a practical engineering character whenever possible, they maintain that at times problems of the so-called academic type have a definite teaching value and so have not hesitated to insert them at strategic points.

The authors wish to acknowledge their indebtedness to Dean R. G. Dukes for reading the manuscript and offering valuable suggestions; to Professor A. P. Poorman, who has been a guiding influence through many years of personal and professional association; and to Professor W. B. Sanders, who has generously devoted considerable time in checking the solutions of all examples and problems.

Acknowledgment is also made of the use for reference purposes of books on mechanics by Poorman, Seely and Ensign, Dodge and Thompson, Boyd, and others.

SEIBERT FAIRMAN
C. S. CUTSHALL
PURDUE UNIVERSITY
June, 1938

CONTENTS

vii

CONTENTS

CHAPTER IV

EQUILIBRIUM OF FORCES IN SPACE

CHAPTER V

FRICTION

CHAPTER VI

CENTROIDS AND CENTER OF GRAVITY

CHAPTER VII

MOMENT OF INERTIA

CHAPTER VIII

RECTILINEAR MOTION

CHAPTER IX

CURVILINEAR MOTION AND ROTATION

CHAPTER XIII

IMPULSE, MOMENTUM, AND IMPACT

ENGINEERING MECHANICS

PART I—STATICS

CHAPTER I

INTRODUCTION; GENERAL PRINCIPLES

Art. 1. The Relation of Mechanics to Engineering. *Mechanics* is that branch of the general science of physics which treats of the action of forces on material bodies. It is usually divided into two parts, *statics* and *kinetics*. *Statics* treats of the relations between forces acting on bodies at rest. *Kinetics* treats of the relations between forces acting on bodies in motion and includes the subject of *kinematics* which deals with pure motion.

Engineering mechanics or *applied mechanics* is the study of the principles of mechanics as applied to problems of engineering. Since the engineer constantly faces problems involving the control of forces and their application to useful purposes, the study of the effects and relations of forces necessarily constitutes an essential part of his preparation. Consequently the subject of mechanics is a basic part of the engineering curriculum and must precede such technical subjects as machine design, structural design, etc.

The study of mechanics is customarily preceded by a course in general physics. A knowledge of the laws, definitions, and principles taken up in the mechanics branch of physics will be assumed throughout this book. Although these fundamental physical concepts will be restated as they arise in the course of the subject, reference should be made to a textbook in general physics if a more detailed discussion is desired. A knowledge of, and ability to use, the various branches of mathematics, including the elementary integral calculus, is also assumed.

Art. 2. Force. *Force* may be defined as that which changes, or tends to change, the state of motion of a body. This conception

of force is involved in the laws of motion as formulated by Sir
Isaac Newton.   They are stated as follows:

1. A body at rest tends to remain at rest, and a body in motion
tends to remain in motion with the same speed in a straight-line
path, unless acted upon externally by some unbalanced force.
This law is the basis of the statics part of mechanics.

2. If a body is acted upon externally by an unbalanced force,
there will result in the motion of the body an acceleration proportional to the force and inversely proportional to the mass of the
body.   This law is the basis of the kinetics part of mechanics.

3. For every force there is an equal, opposite, and collinear
reaction.   That is, a single force cannot exist alone; or a body
cannot exert a force on another without receiving an equal force in
return.

The *resultant* of a system of forces is a single force which, acting
alone, will produce the same effect as the system.   The *equilibrant*
of a system of forces is a single force which, if added to the system,
would balance or neutralize the system.   It follows that the resultant and equilibrant are equal, opposite, and collinear.

The *components* of a force are two or more forces which, acting
together, have an effect identical to that of the given force.   Hence,
a force is the resultant of its components.

The *moment* of a force is the measure of its turning or twisting
effect about a given axis and is determined by the product of the
force and its perpendicular distance from the axis.

A *vector* is a physical quantity which involves a sense of direction as well as magnitude.   Any vector may be represented graphically by a straight line whose length represents to some chosen
scale the magnitude of the vector and which has an arrowhead at
one end to designate the direction.   A force is not completely specified without giving both its magnitude and direction and is therefore a vector quantity.   Other examples of vector quantities are
displacement, velocity, acceleration, momentum, etc.

A physical quantity which involves magnitude but no sense of
direction is known as a *scalar* quantity.   Time, for instance, does
not have direction and is therefore a scalar quantity.   Other examples of scalar quantities are mass, work, energy, etc.

Art. 3. Fundamental Laws Governing Forces.   The following
laws are developed in general physics and are briefly restated here
without further proof.

The Parallelogram Law. If two coplanar, concurrent forces are laid out vectorially with both forces pointing toward or both away from their point of intersection and the parallelogram is completed upon the forces as sides, the diagonal of the parallelogram, drawn from the point of intersection, represents completely the resultant of the forces. In Fig. 1, A and B represent the two forces upon which the parallelogram is constructed. The diagonal R is the resultant of the forces. This process, which can be applied to any vector quantities, is known as geometric or vectorial addition.

The Triangle Law. If two coplanar, concurrent forces are laid out vectorially with the beginning of the second at the end of the first, the vector extending from the beginning of the first to the end of the second, thus forming the third side of a triangle, repre-

Fig. 1.   Fig. 2.

sents completely the resultant of the forces. In Fig. 2 are shown the same forces A and B of Fig. 1, laid out with their resultant R to form a triangle. By a comparison of the two figures it is readily seen that the triangle of Fig. 2 is in reality a portion of the parallelogram of Fig. 1. The triangle law is thus a corollary of the parallelogram law.

The Polygon Law. When it is desired to obtain the resultant of more than two coplanar, concurrent forces, either the parallelogram or triangle law may be applied, any two of the forces being combined into their resultant which is in turn combined with a third force, and so on until all the forces have been included. The use of the triangle law in such a manner leads to the polygon law: If the forces of a system of any number of coplanar, concurrent forces are laid off consecutively as vectors with the beginning of each vector at the end of the preceding one, the vector extending from the beginning of the first force to the end of the last, thus forming the closing side of a polygon, represents completely the resultant of the system. In Fig. 3 are shown four forces A, B, C, and D. The resultant R_1 of forces A and B is obtained by means of the triangle law.   Force C and resultant R_1 are similarly combined into their resultant R_2.   Finally, force D and resultant R_2 combine to give R_3, which is the resultant of the entire system. It is now obvious that the intermediate resultants R_1 and R_2 are unnecessary.   If they are removed from the figure, a polygon remains.   It should be noted that, in the polygon, the forces follow each other in direction around the polygon, whereas their resultant points in the opposite direction.   If the vector representing the resultant were reversed in direction so as to follow the forces, it would then represent the *equilibrant* of the system.

Fig. 3.

According to the law of *transmissibility of forces*, a force may be transmitted any distance along its line of action without changing its effect.   However, a force cannot be shifted out of its line of action without altering its effect.

Art. 4.   Resolution of a Force.   A force may be resolved into two components by applying the principles stated in Art. 3.   The application of the principle may be made by graphical, trigonometric, or algebraic methods.

(a) *Graphical Method.*   This method involves laying out forces vectorially to a suitable scale and constructing geometric figures. For instance, to determine the components of a force, the given force may be laid out as a vector and a parallelogram constructed with this vector as a diagonal.   The sides of the parallelogram then represent the required components.   It is obvious that an infinite number of parallelograms may be constructed with a given line as a diagonal.   It is therefore necessary to specify the lines of action of the components desired.

Example 1

The force F in Fig. 4 is 400 lb. and is to be resolved into two components whose action lines make angles of 30° and 105°, respectively, with F. Determine the components.

Solution: The force F is laid out to some convenient scale as shown in Fig. 4. Through one end of F, lines are drawn at 30° and 105° with F. Parallel lines are drawn through the other end of F so as to complete a parallelogram with F as the diagonal.

Fig. 4.

The sides C_1 and C_2 constitute the required components and scale 546 lb. and 283 lb. respectively.

If the action lines of the desired components are to be at right angles with each other, the parallelogram becomes a rectangle and the components are known as rectangular components. Since it is possible to construct an infinite number of rectangles upon a given diagonal, it becomes necessary to specify the direction of such components. The graphical construction is then similar to Example 1 above.

(b) *Trigonometric Method.* In the trigonometric method of resolving a force into its components, the parallelogram or triangle may be sketched free-hand and the laws of trigonometry then applied to determine the components.

Example 2

Solve Example 1 by the trigonometric method.

Fig. 5.

Solution: The triangle, consisting of F and its components C_1 and C_2, is sketched and the angles indicated as shown in Fig. 5. By the sine law:

$$\frac{C_1}{\sin 105°} = \frac{400}{\sin 45°} \quad \text{and} \quad \frac{C_2}{\sin 30°} = \frac{400}{\sin 45°}$$

whence $C_1 = 546$ lb. and $C_2 = 283$ lb.

It should be noted that, in this method of solution, it is not necessary to draw forces to scale or to lay out the angles exactly.

Example 3

FIG. 6.

The force F in Fig. 6 is to be resolved into its vertical and horizontal components, F_V and F_H.

Solution: From the trigonometry of the right-angle triangle of Fig. 6,

$$F_V = 500 \sin 35° = 287 \text{ lb.}$$
$$F_H = 500 \cos 35° = 410 \text{ lb.}$$

Example 4

The line of action of force F in Fig. 7 passes through points O and A, as shown. Determine the vertical and horizontal components of this force.

Solution: The distance OA is first computed.

FIG. 7.

$$OA = \sqrt{(4)^2 + (2)^2} = 4.47$$

Then, by trigonometry,

$$F_V = 80 \sin \alpha = 80 \times \frac{2}{4.47} = 35.8 \text{ lb.}$$

$$F_H = 80 \cos \alpha = 80 \times \frac{4}{4.47} = 71.6 \text{ lb.}$$

It should be noted in this case that it is not necessary to determine the value of angle α.

Problems

(The following problems should be solved trigonometrically and checked graphically.)

1. Resolve a 1200-lb. force acting at 15° with the horizontal into its vertical and horizontal components.   *Ans.* $F_V = 311$ lb.; $F_H = 1160$ lb.

2. Resolve a 700-lb. force into components acting at 15° and 40° with the force.   *Ans.* $C_1 = 550$ lb.; $C_2 = 221$ lb.

3. A force of 850 lb. acts through the origin and a point whose coordinates are $x = 15$, $y = 8$. Determine the x and y components of the force.   *Ans.* $F_x = 750$ lb.; $F_y = 400$ lb.

4. A force of 2500 lb. acts at an angle of 60° with the x axis. Resolve this force into components acting at 105° and 330°, respectively, with the x axis.   *Ans.* $C_1 = 3540$ lb.; $C_2 = 2500$ lb.

Art. 5. Composition of Coplanar, Concurrent Forces. The resultant of a system of coplanar, concurrent forces may be determined by graphical, trigonometric, or algebraic methods.

(*a*) *Graphical Method.* The principle of this method has already been explained in Art. 3. If only two forces are to be combined, either the parallelogram or triangle law may be used. If more than two forces are to be combined, the application of either parallelogram or triangle laws may prove to be unnecessarily tedious and the polygon law may then be used to advantage. In laying out the polygon, the forces may be taken in any order.

Example 1

Determine the magnitude of the resultant of the four forces shown in Fig. 8 (*a*) and its angle θ_H with the horizontal.

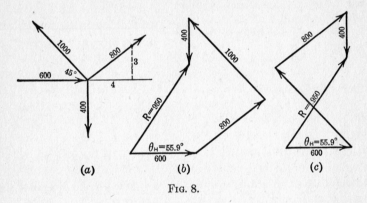

(*a*)   (*b*)   (*c*)

FIG. 8.

Solution: The forces are laid out in order to some convenient scale as shown in Fig. 8 (*b*). The resultant R is the closing side of the polygon and scales 950 lb. The angle θ_H scales 55.9°.

Fig. 8 (*c*) shows the same forces laid out in a different order without changing the final results.

(*b*) *Trigonometric Method.* When the resultant of only two forces is required, the parallelogram or triangle may be sketched free-hand and the resultant obtained by means of the laws of trigonometry.

Example 2

Determine the resultant of the 50-lb. and 80-lb. forces shown in Fig. 9.
Solution: By the law of cosines:

$$R^2 = (50)^2 + (80)^2 + 2(50)(80) \cos 120° \quad R = 70 \text{ lb.}$$

$$\theta = \tan^{-1} \frac{50 \sin 120°}{80 + 50 \cos 120°} = 38.3°$$

When there are more than two forces to be combined, the above procedure becomes tedious and cumbersome. The algebraic method which follows is preferable in such problems.

Fig. 9.

(c) *Algebraic Method.* It was shown in Art. 4, Ex. 3 and 4, that a force may easily be resolved trignonometrically into horizontal and vertical components. If every force in a given system is subjected to this process, the original system is thus replaced by an equivalent system containing two groups of forces, one consisting of forces having a common line of action in the horizontal direction, and the other consisting of forces having a common vertical line of action. The resultant of the horizontal group is their algebraic sum, represented by the symbol ΣF_H. The resultant of the vertical group is their algebraic sum, represented by the symbol ΣF_V. The resultant of the original system of forces is therefore:

$$\mathbf{R} = \sqrt{(\Sigma \mathbf{F}_H)^2 + (\Sigma \mathbf{F}_V)^2}$$

and its angle with the horizontal is

$$\theta_H = \tan^{-1} \frac{\Sigma \mathbf{F}_V}{\Sigma \mathbf{F}_H}$$

Example 3

Solve Example 1 of this article, using the algebraic method.
Solution: For convenience, the forces are shown again in Fig. 10 (a). Taking direction to the right as positive, to the left as negative, upward as positive, and downward as negative, the summations of horizontal and vertical components are made.

$$\Sigma F_H = 800 \times \tfrac{4}{5} + 600 - 1000 \cos 45° = + 533 \text{ lb.}$$
$$\Sigma F_V = 800 \times \tfrac{3}{5} + 1000 \sin 45° - 400 = + 787 \text{ lb.}$$

(a) (b)

FIG. 10:

These results are shown in Fig. 10 (b), from which

$$R = \sqrt{(787)^2 + (533)^2} = 950 \text{ lb.}$$

$$\theta_H = \tan^{-1} \frac{787}{533} = 55.9°$$

Problems

(Graphic, trigonometric, or algebraic methods may be used in the following problems. Select the method which seems most convenient for the problem under consideration.)

1. Determine the amount of the resultant of the two forces shown in Fig. 11, and its angle with the horizontal. *Ans.* $R = 275$ lb.; $\theta_H = 49.1°$.

FIG. 11.   FIG: 12.

2. Determine the amount and direction of the resultant of the three forces shown in Fig. 12.   *Ans.* $R = 605$ lb.; $\theta_x = 51.3°$.

3. Determine the value of angle θ and the force F necessary to balance the two forces shown in Fig. 13.   *Ans.* $F = 2690$ lb.; $\theta = 21.8°$.

FIG. 13.   FIG. 14.

4. Determine the amount and direction of the resultant of the four forces shown in Fig. 14.   *Ans.* $R = 1160$ lb.; $\theta_x = 143.9°$.

5. Determine the amount and direction of the resultant of the five forces shown in Fig. 15.   *Ans.* $R = 816$ lb.; $\theta_x = 219.6°$.

FIG. 15.   FIG. 16.

6. In Fig. 16, the resultant of the four forces shown is to be 500 lb. acting horizontally toward the right. Determine the required values of F and θ.   *Ans.* $F = 1290$ lb.; $\theta = 70.5°$.

Art. 6. Composition and Resolution of Coplanar, Parallel Forces; Force Couples.

The resultant of any number of parallel forces must occupy a line of action parallel to those of its components, and its magnitude must be the algebraic sum of the forces composing the system, the direction being indicated by the sign of their algebraic sum. The position of the resultant with respect to its components may now be determined either algebraically or graphically.

(a) *Algebraic Method.* The location of the resultant is obtained by applying the principle that the moment of the resultant with respect to any given axis must equal the algebraic sum of the moments of the components with respect to the same axis. The entire process may be expressed algebraically as follows:

$$\mathbf{R} = \Sigma\mathbf{F}$$

$$\mathbf{R \cdot r} = \Sigma\mathbf{M} = \mathbf{F_1 r_1} + \mathbf{F_2 r_2} + \mathbf{F_3 r_3} \cdots$$

where r represents the distance of R from the axis of moments; and r_1 the distance of F_1 from the same axis, etc.

Example 1

Determine the amount and location of the resultant of the three parallel forces shown in Fig. 17.

Solution: Taking upward as positive in direction, the summation of forces gives

$$R = \Sigma F = 20 - 50 - 30 = -60 \text{ lb.}$$

The resultant is therefore directed downwards. To determine its location, let point O be selected as the axis of moments and let clockwise moments be taken as positive. Then

Fig. 17.

$$60 \times r = \Sigma M_O = 20 \times 7 - 50 \times 1 - 30 \times 0 = +90$$

$$r = 1.5 \text{ ft.}$$

Fig. 18.

(b) *Graphic Method.* The principle of moments is also used in devising a graphic method of locating the resultant. In Fig. 18, A and B are two parallel forces in the same direction; a and b are their respective distances from the resultant R. By moments with respect to any point on the line of action of R

$$R \times 0 = \Sigma M = A \times a - B \times b$$

or

$$\frac{A}{B} = \frac{b}{a}$$

This result shows that the resultant of two parallel forces in the same direction divides the distance between them in inverse proportion to the forces.

Any straight line m–n, known as a base line, is now drawn so as to intersect the forces A and B, as shown in Fig. 19. A

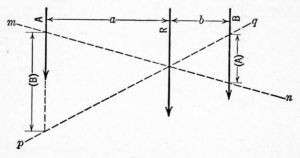

FIG. 19.

length, representing force A to scale, is laid off on the line of action of force B on one side of the base line. A length, representing force B to scale, is laid off on the line of action of force A but on the opposite side of the base line. The ends of these lengths are now connected by the diagonal, p–q. The intersection of p–q and m–n locates the position of R since, by similar triangles resulting from the construction,

$$\frac{A}{B} = \frac{b}{a}$$

as required. The resultant is seen to lie between the forces, on the side of the larger force.

The same procedure is followed in combining two parallel forces acting in opposite directions except that the distances representing the forces must be laid off on the same side of the base line. The construction for this case, Fig. 20, shows the resultant to lie outside the forces on the side of the larger component.

The graphic method just outlined above is called the method of inverse proportion. Only two forces at a time may be combined by this method. If more than two parallel forces are to be combined into their resultant, the inverse proportion method may be used to combine any two of the forces, whose resultant is then combined with a third force, and so on until all the forces have been accounted for. Other graphical methods are available for accomplishing the same result but are considered to lie outside the scope of this book. For further details reference should be made to some textbook designed particularly for graphic methods.[1]

FIG. 20.

The resolution of a force into two components parallel to itself may be accomplished algebraically by procedure similar to that in part (a) above, keeping in mind that the action lines of the components must be specified; otherwise, an infinite number of solutions would be possible.

Example 2

Resolve the force P shown in Fig. 21 into two components parallel to itself and acting at distances of 5 inches and 7 inches from P on the same side.

Solution: Let C_1 and C_2 represent the required components. Then, since $R = \Sigma F$,

FIG. 21.

$$50 = C_1 + C_2 \qquad (1)$$

With point O as center of moments, the equation $R \cdot r = \Sigma M$ becomes

$$50 \times 5 = C_1 \times 0 - C_2 \times 2 \qquad (2)$$

Solution of equations (1) and (2) gives $C_1 = 175$ lb. and $C_2 = -125$ lb. The negative result shows that C_2 must act in the direction opposite to that shown in the figure.

The resolution of a force into two components parallel to itself may be accomplished graphically by the inverse proportion method already explained.

[1] Fairman and Cutshall, "Graphic Statics," McGraw-Hill Book Co., New York, 1932.

Example 3

Solve Example 2 graphically by the method of inverse proportion.

Solution: The distances between the force and its components are laid out to scale as shown in Fig. 22. Any convenient base line $m-n$ is

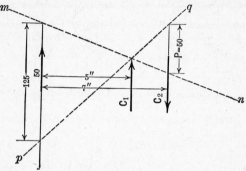

FIG. 22.

drawn, intersecting the forces. The value of P is now laid off on the line of action of either component, say C_2, starting from the base line. A diagonal $p-q$ is then drawn from the other end of the length representing P and through the intersection of $m-n$ with C_1. The distance along the line of action of P between the lines $m-n$ and $p-q$ now represents the value of C_2 and scales 125 lb. The value of $C_1 = 175$ lb. then follows by algebraic summation.

A special situation sometimes arises in connection with parallel forces. When two equal but oppositely directed parallel forces are

FIG. 23.

combined, the resultant is zero but the sum of the moments will not be zero. Such a pair of forces is known as a *force couple* and possesses certain important properties.

In Fig. 23 is shown a force couple consisting of two forces, each of value F, located at any distance d apart. Let O be any point located at distance x from one of the forces. Then

$$\Sigma M_O = F(x + d) - F \cdot x = F \cdot d.$$

Hence, the moment Fd of the force couple does not involve the distance x and therefore is independent of the position of the axis of rotation. The following propositions regarding force couples may then be deduced.

1. The moment of a force couple is always the product of one of the forces and the distance between them.

2. The moment of a force couple is independent of the position of the axis of moments.

3. A force couple may be moved to any other position in its plane or a parallel plane without changing its effect.

4. A force couple can be balanced only by the addition of another force couple of equal but opposite moment.

Problems

1. Determine the amount and position of the resultant of the forces shown in Fig. 24.

Ans. $R = 1300$ lb. acting downward at 5.38 ft. to the right of the 800-lb. force.

FIG. 24.   FIG. 25.

2. Resolve the force shown in Fig. 25 into parallel components A and B.
Ans. $A = 720$ lb. down; $B = 480$ lb. down.

3. Resolve the force shown in Fig. 26 into parallel components A and B.
Ans. $A = 720$ lb. up; $B = 1320$ lb. down.

FIG. 26.   FIG. 27.

4. Determine the amount and position of the resultant of the parallel forces shown in Fig. 27.

Ans. $R = 15$ lb. up at 16 in. to the left of the 75-lb. force.

FIG. 28.

5. Determine the amount and position of the resultant of the system of parallel forces shown in Fig. 28.

Ans. $R = 900$ lb. down at 6.56 in. to the right of the 200-lb. force.

6. Determine the resultant of the force system shown in Fig. 29.

Ans. A force couple having clockwise moment of 750 in.-lb.

FIG. 29.

Art. 7. Composition of Coplanar, Non-concurrent, Non-parallel Forces.

To describe the resultant of a general system of forces in a plane completely, its magnitude, its angle with some given line, and its position or distance from a given point must be stated. The magnitude and angle with a given line may be determined by graphic or algebraic methods as previously demonstrated in Art. 5. If successive parallelograms were used in obtaining the resultant graphically, the diagonal of the final parallelogram determines the position of the resultant of the system.   Algebraically, the position of the resultant is determined by applying the principle of moments.

Example

Determine completely the resultant of the three forces acting on the pole shown in Fig. 30.

Solution: In the graphical solution shown in Fig. 31, the structure is

FIG. 30.   FIG. 31.

first laid out to scale. Then the 2500-lb. and 1000-lb. forces are combined by the parallelogram method into their resultant R_1 which scales 2693 lb. This resultant is similarly combined with the 3000-lb. force to obtain R_2, the resultant of the entire system, which scales 5380 lb. Its angle with the horizontal, θ_H, scales 48°, and its perpendicular distance r from the foot of the pole scales 9.2 ft. The distance from the foot of the pole to the point where the resultant intersects it scales 13.8 ft.

The algebraic solution of the above example is made as follows:

$$\Sigma F_H = 3000 \sin 60° + 1000 = 3600 \text{ lb.}$$
$$\Sigma F_V = -3000 \cos 60° - 2500 = -4000 \text{ lb.}$$
$$R_2 = \sqrt{(3600)^2 + (4000)^2} = 5380 \text{ lb.}$$

$$\theta_H = \tan^{-1}\frac{4000}{3600} = 48°$$

$$r = \frac{\Sigma M_A}{R} = \frac{3000 \sin 60° \times 20 + 1000 \times 10 - 2500 \times 5}{5380} = 9.2 \text{ ft.}$$

The distance from the point where R_2 cuts the pole to the foot is

$$\frac{9.2}{\cos 48°} = 13.8 \text{ ft.}$$

Problems

1. Determine completely the resultant of the three forces acting on the double pulley shown in Fig. 32.

Ans. $R = 1250$ lb. acting downward through the center at 315.8° with the horizontal.

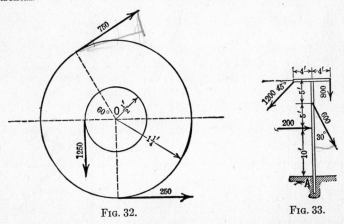

FIG. 32.   FIG. 33.

2. Determine the resultant of the four forces acting on the pole shown in Fig. 33.

Ans. $R = 2200$ lb.; $\theta_H = 260.9°$; intersects ground at 4.94 ft. to left of A.

3. A mill-bent is acted upon by forces as shown in Fig. 34. Determine the resultant, its angle with the horizontal, and the distance from A to the point where it intersects line AB. (Suggestion: As a preliminary step, combine each group of parallel forces into its resultant by inspection.)

Ans. $R = 14{,}600$ lb.; $\theta_H = 288.4°$; 32 ft.

Fig. 34.

Art. 8. Resolution and Composition of Non-coplanar, Concurrent Forces.
A convenient method used to diagram a force in

Fig. 35.

space is shown in Fig. 35. The components of the force parallel to the coordinate axes in space are easily obtained as follows:

$$F_x = F \cos \alpha$$
$$F_y = F \cos \beta$$
$$F_z = F \cos \gamma$$

In many cases, the angles α, β, and γ are not given directly, but the direction of the force is specified by stating the coordinates of two

points in space through which it passes. This is shown in Fig. 36.
To obtain values of cos α, cos β, and cos γ, the length of the diagonal OA is computed. The components are then readily obtained.

Example 1

Let the force F in Fig. 36 be 200 lb. Determine its x, y, and z com
ponents.

FIG. 36.

Solution: $OA = \sqrt{(12)^2 + (10)^2 + (7)^2} = 17.1$

Then $F_x = 200 \cos \alpha = 200 \times \dfrac{12}{17.1} = 140.3 \text{ lb.}$

$F_y = 200 \cos \beta = 200 \times \dfrac{10}{17.1} = 117.0 \text{ lb.}$

$F_z = 200 \cos \gamma = 200 \times \dfrac{7}{17.1} = 81.9 \text{ lb.}$

The resultant of any number of concurrent forces in space may
now be determined by first resolving each force in the system into
its x, y, and z components as shown above. The x components are
then added algebraically to obtain their sum ΣF_x. Similarly,
ΣF_y and ΣF_z are obtained. Finally, the magnitude of the resultant is

$$\mathbf{R} = \sqrt{(\Sigma \mathbf{F_x})^2 + (\Sigma \mathbf{F_y})^2 + (\Sigma \mathbf{F_z})^2}$$

and its direction in space is given by

$$\cos \alpha = \frac{\Sigma \mathbf{F_x}}{\mathbf{R}}; \ \cos \beta = \frac{\Sigma \mathbf{F_y}}{\mathbf{R}}; \ \cos \gamma = \frac{\Sigma \mathbf{F_z}}{\mathbf{R}}$$

Example 2

Determine the resultant of the three forces shown in Fig. 37.

FIG. 37.

Solution: The three diagonals are first determined.

$$OA = \sqrt{(12)^2 + (6)^2 + (6)^2} = 14.7$$

$$OB = \sqrt{(8)^2 + (10)^2 + (4)^2} = 13.4$$

$$OC = \sqrt{(11)^2 + (4)^2 + (8)^2} = 14.2$$

Summations of components along each of the three coordinate axes are now made.

$$\Sigma F_x = 80 \times \frac{12}{14.7} + 60 \times \frac{8}{13.4} + 20 \times - \frac{11}{14.2} = 85.6 \text{ lb.}$$

$$\Sigma F_y = 80 \times \frac{6}{14.7} + 60 \times \frac{10}{13.4} + 20 \times \frac{4}{14.2} = 83.1 \text{ lb.}$$

$$\Sigma F_z = 80 \times \frac{6}{14.7} + 60 \times \frac{4}{13.4} + 20 \times \frac{8}{14.2} = 61.8 \text{ lb.}$$

These values are now combined to obtain:

$$R = \sqrt{(85.6)^2 + (83.1)^2 + (61.8)^2} = 134.5 \text{ lb.}$$

$$\alpha = \cos^{-1} \frac{85.6}{134.5} = 50.5°$$

$$\beta = \cos^{-1} \frac{83.1}{134.5} = 51.8°$$

$$\gamma = \cos^{-1} \frac{61.8}{134.5} = 62.7°$$

Problems

1. A force of 150 lb. passes through the origin and a point in space whose coordinates are (5,4,3). Compute the x, y, and z components of the force.

Ans. 106; 84.8; 63.6.

FIG. 38.

2. Determine the amount and direction in space of the resultant of the three forces shown in Fig. 38.

Ans. $R = 230$ lb.; $\alpha = 54.9°$; $\beta = 81.8°$; $\gamma = 35.9°$.

FIG. 39.

3. Determine the amount and direction in space of the resultant of the four forces shown in Fig. 39.

Ans. $R = 61.6$ lb.; $\alpha = 223.8°$; $\beta = 226.4°$; $\gamma = 266.5°$.

Art. 9. Composition of Non-coplanar Parallel Forces.

The resultant of any number of parallel forces in space is equal in magnitude to the algebraic sum of the forces, it must be parallel to the forces, and its position in space must be such that its moment with respect to any axis in space is equal to the sum of the moments of the forces with respect to the same axis.

Example

Determine the amount and position of the resultant of the three parallel forces shown in Fig. 40.

FIG. 40.

Solution: Coordinate axes are chosen as shown in Fig. 40. The magnitude and direction of the resultant are first determined by

$$R = \Sigma F = 80 + 50 - 30 = + 100 \text{ lb. (upward)}$$

Let the position of R be denoted by the coordinates $\bar{x}$ and $\bar{z}$. Then since

$$R \cdot \bar{z} = \Sigma M_x \quad \text{and} \quad R \cdot \bar{x} = \Sigma M_z,$$
$$100 \cdot \bar{z} = 80 \times 4 + 50 \times 1 + 30 \times 5$$
$$100 \cdot \bar{x} = 80 \times 2 + 50 \times 6 - 30 \times 3$$

from which $\bar{x} = 3.7$ ft.   and $\bar{z} = 5.2$ ft.

Problems

1. Determine the magnitude, direction, and location of the resultant of the three parallel forces shown in Fig. 41.

Ans. $R = 250$ lb. down; $\bar{x} = 0.36$ ft.; $\bar{z} = 1.84$ ft.

2. A rectangular platform 10 ft. long and 6 ft. wide carries loads of 1200 lb. at its center, 200 lb. midway between the corners at one of the 6-ft. ends, and 300 lb. midway between the corners at one of the 10-ft. sides. Determine the amount and position of the resultant load.

Ans. $R = 1700$ lb. acting at 4.41 ft. from the end and 2.47 ft. from the side.

FIG. 41.

Art. 10. Composition of Non-coplanar, Non-parallel, Non-concurrent Forces.

The resultant effect of the general system of forces in space usually is not a single force but consists of a force and a couple. The force may be taken through any point in space, and the couple may be represented by component couples acting in convenient planes. It is convenient to select the point through which the resultant force acts as the origin of a set of coordinate axes; the magnitude of the resultant force and its angles with the coordinate axes are then determined, and finally the resultant couple is obtained by means of its component couples with respect to each of the three axes.

Example

Determine the resultant effect of the two forces shown in Fig. 42 (a).

Solution: It is first necessary to resolve each force into x, y, and z

FIG. 42.

components by the method of Art. 8. The distances $A\dot{B}$ and CD are therefore determined:

$$AB = \sqrt{8^2 + 6^2 + 2^2} = 10.2$$
$$CD = \sqrt{5^2 + 6^2 + 4^2} = 8.78$$

The components of force AB are thus:

$$AB_x = 600 \times \frac{8}{10.2} = +471 \text{ lb.}$$

$$AB_y = 600 \times \frac{-6}{10.2} = -353 \text{ lb.}$$

$$AB_z = 600 \times \frac{-2}{10.2} = -118 \text{ lb.}$$

and the components of force CD are:

$$CD_x = 400 \times \frac{-5}{8.78} = -228 \text{ lb.}$$

$$CD_y = 400 \times \frac{6}{8.78} = +274 \text{ lb.}$$

$$CD_z = 400 \times \frac{-4}{8.78} = -182 \text{ lb.}$$

These components are shown in Fig. 42 (b). From the above results:

$$\Sigma F_x = +243 \text{ lb.;} \quad \Sigma F_y = -79 \text{ lb.;} \quad \Sigma F_z = -300 \text{ lb.}$$

The resultant force through O may now be computed:

$$R = \sqrt{(243)^2 + (79)^2 + (300)^2} = 394 \text{ lb.}$$

The direction of R in space is determined by:

$$\alpha = \cos^{-1} \frac{\Sigma F_x}{R} = \cos^{-1} \frac{243}{394} = 308°$$

$$\beta = \cos^{-1} \frac{\Sigma F_y}{R} = \cos^{-1} \frac{-79}{394} = 101.5°$$

$$\gamma = \cos^{-1} \frac{\Sigma F_z}{R} = \cos^{-1} \frac{-300}{394} = 139.5°$$

The above angles are measured from the positive ends of the respective axes.

It now remains to determine the component moment of the resultant force couple with respect to each coordinate axis. This is most conveniently obtained by summation of the moments with respect to a given axis of the x, y, and z components of the original forces. The components of a given force may be placed at any point along the line of action of the force. In the steps which follow, the components of the 600-lb. force will be taken as acting at point A, and those of the 400-lb. force at point C, as shown in Fig. 42 (b). In obtaining the moments, counterclockwise rotation, as viewed from the positive end of the axis toward the origin, will be taken as positive. Thus,

$$\Sigma M_x = 471 \times 0 + 353 \times 4 - 118 \times 6 + 228 \times 0 - 274 \times 4 + 182 \times 0$$
$$= -392 \text{ ft-lb.}$$
$$\Sigma M_y = 471 \times 4 + 353 \times 0 + 118 \times 0 - 228 \times 4 + 274 \times 0 + 182 \times 8$$
$$= +2428 \text{ ft-lb.}$$
$$\Sigma M_z = -471 \times 6 + 353 \times 0 + 118 \times 0 + 228 \times 0 + 274 \times 8 + 182 \times 0$$
$$= -634 \text{ ft-lb.}$$

A force couple or moment is a vector quantity and may be represented by a vector perpendicular to the plane of the couple. Thus the above results may be combined vectorially into a resultant force couple and the direction in space of the axis of rotation of the couple may be determined. However, it is ordinarily sufficient to state the component couples as given above.

Problems

1. Combine the three forces shown in Fig. 43 into a single force through O and a couple.

Fig. 43.

Ans. $R = 70.7$ lb.; $\alpha = 55.6°$; $\beta = 45°$; $\gamma = 64.9°$; $\Sigma M_x = +90$ ft-lb.; $\Sigma M_y = +160$ ft-lb.; $\Sigma M_z = +250$ ft-lb.

2. Determine the resultant effect of the two forces shown in Fig. 44.

Ans. $R = 473$ lb.; $\alpha = 86.1°$; $\beta = 59.1°$; $\gamma = 31.1°$; $\Sigma M_x = 0$; $\Sigma M_y = -648$ ft-lb.; $\Sigma M_z = 390$ ft-lb.

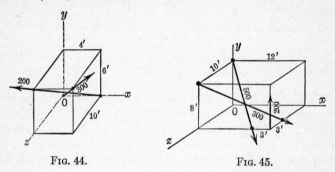

FIG. 44.   FIG. 45.

3. Determine the resultant effect of the force system shown in Fig. 45.

Ans. $R = 630$ lb.; $\alpha = 32.5°$; $\beta = 110.2°$; $\gamma = 65.8°$; $\Sigma M_x = 1690$ ft-lb.; $\Sigma M_y = 2440$ ft-lb.; $\Sigma M_z = -1850$ ft-lb.

CHAPTER II

EQUILIBRIUM OF COPLANAR FORCES

Art. 11. Equilibrium and the Free Body. A body is said to be in *equilibrium* when it is in a state of rest or is moving with constant speed in a straight-line path. Likewise, the system of all forces acting externally on such a body is in equilibrium. Under such conditions the resultant of all the forces in the system must be zero and the algebraic sum of the moments of all the forces about any axis must be zero.

In the solution of problems in statics involving determination of unknown quantities, it is found convenient to select some object which is acted upon by the forces in question, isolate it from its surroundings, and then consider the equilibrium of the system of forces acting externally upon the object. Such an object, separated from other objects with which it may be in contact, is known as a *free body*. If the free body is in equilibrium, all the forces acting upon it compose a system in equilibrium to which certain methods of solution may then be applied. It should particularly be noted, however, that internal forces (that is, forces acting within the free body itself) have no effect on the motion of the body and therefore are not involved when the equilibrium of the body is considered.

Art. 12. The Conditions of Equilibrium. A system of forces known to be in equilibrium must satisfy the following conditions:

(1) The forces when laid out vectorially must form a closed polygon. This follows from Art. 3, in which it is shown that the vector necessary to cause a polygon of forces to close represents the resultant or the equilibrant of the system.

(2) The algebraic summation of the components of the forces in any assigned direction of resolution must be zero. This condition is expressed by the equations:

$$\Sigma F_x = 0 \quad \text{and} \quad \Sigma F_y = 0$$

where x and y represent any arbitrarily chosen axes. This follows

27

from Art. 5 (c), where it is shown that $R = \sqrt{(\Sigma F_x)^2 + (\Sigma F_y)^2}$. When $R = 0$, it is necessary that $\Sigma F_x = 0$ and $\Sigma F_y = 0$.

(3) The algebraic summation of the moments of the forces with respect to any assigned axis must equal zero, or $\Sigma M = 0$. If this condition were not fulfilled, rotation of the body would occur, and equilibrium could not exist.

(4) If three non-parallel forces are in equilibrium, they must be *concurrent*. This follows from the fact that the resultant of any two of the forces must be collinear with the third.

Art. 13. The Solution of the General Problem of Equilibrium. The analysis and solution of any problem involving equilibrium require the following steps:

(1) Selection of the free body.

(2) A diagram of the free body showing all dimensions and external forces. The values of all known forces and dimensions should be indicated and some system of notation by letters used to designate those forces or dimensions unknown in value.

(3) Application of one or more of the conditions of equilibrium laid down in the previous article to determine the various unknowns required.

Art. 14. Concurrent Forces in Equilibrium. The solution of this type of problem may be carried out graphically, by laying out the force polygon vectorially; or algebraically, by means of the equations $\Sigma F_x = 0$, $\Sigma F_y = 0$, and $\Sigma M = 0$. When no more than three forces are involved, the force polygon becomes a triangle which may then be solved trigonometrically.

A concurrent coplanar system of forces must involve no more than two unknowns; otherwise it will be found that there are not sufficient independent conditions of equilibrium to make possible a solution. Such a system, incapable of solution by applying the static conditions of equilibrium, is known as statically indeterminate.

Example 1

Determine the force P, acting at 45° with the horizontal, required to start the wheel shown in Fig. 46 (a) over the block.

Solution: (a) *Graphical Method.* The free body, Fig. 46 (b), consists of the wheel itself, acted upon by three external forces, the weight of the wheel acting vertically downward through its center, the force P, and the reaction R_A of the block against the wheel. Since the three forces are not parallel they must be *concurrent*, and so the reaction R_A must pass through O, the center of the wheel.   The angle AOB is found to be 60°. The force polygon is then laid out as shown in Fig. 46 (*c*), from which P scales 179 lb. and R_A scales 146 lb.

FIG. 46.

(*b*) *Trigonometric Method.*   Since the force polygon in this example is a triangle, a trigonometric solution is possible.   By use of the sine law:

$$\frac{P}{\sin 60°} = \frac{200}{\sin 75°} = \frac{R_A}{\sin 45°}$$

from which $P = 179$ lb. and $R_A = 146$ lb.

(*c*) *Algebraic method.*   Let x and y axes be taken in the horizontal and vertical directions as shown in Fig. 46 (*b*).   Then

$$\Sigma F_x = P \cos 45° - R_A \cos 30° = 0 \tag{1}$$
$$\Sigma F_y = P \sin 45° + R_A \sin 30° - 200 = 0 \tag{2}$$

Simultaneous solution of (1) and (2) gives results for P and R_A identical with those already stated.

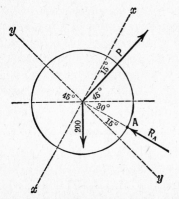

FIG. 47.

Simultaneous equations may be avoided by placing the axes so that each is perpendicular to one of the unknowns, as shown in Fig. 47. The following equations are now obtained:

$$\Sigma F_x = P \cos 15° - 200 \cos 30° = 0 \qquad P = 179 \text{ lb.}$$
$$\Sigma F_y = R_A \cos 15° - 200 \cos 45° = 0 \qquad R_A = 146 \text{ lb.}$$

This process is known as shifting the axes.

Example 2

Two cylinders, A and B, rest in a box as shown in Fig. 48 (a). A has a diameter of 10 in. and weighs 200 lb. B has a diameter of 18 in. and weighs 500 lb. The box is 18 in. wide. Determine the pressures at all points of contact.

Solution: The dimension AB is seen by inspection to be 14 in. The distance HG is 9 tan 30° = 5.19 in. BC is therefore 18 − 5 − 5.19 = 7.81 in., and AC becomes $\sqrt{(14)^2 - (7.81)^2} = 11.6$ in. Thus, the functions of angle θ are $\sin \theta = 7.81/14 = 0.558$ and $\cos \theta = 11.6/14 = 0.828$.

Fig. 48.

Cylinder A is selected as the first free body as shown in Fig. 48 (b). Solving algebraically:

$$\Sigma F_V = D \cos \theta - 200 = 0 \qquad D = 242 \text{ lb.}$$
$$\Sigma F_H = E - 242 \sin \theta = 0 \qquad E = 135 \text{ lb.}$$

The solution of this free body may also be made graphically or trigonometrically. The cylinder B is now taken as a free body, as shown in Fig. 48 (c). Solving algebraically:

$$\Sigma F_H = F \sin 60° - 242 \sin \theta = 0 \qquad\qquad F = 156 \text{ lb.}$$
$$\Sigma F_V = G + 156 \cos 60° - 500 - 242 \cos \theta = 0 \qquad G = 622 \text{ lb.}$$

The solution of this free body may also be made graphically.

Problems

1. Determine the forces exerted by the members AB and BC of Fig. 49.

Ans. $AB = 896$ lb.; $BC = 732$ lb.

FIG. 49.

FIG. 50.

2. The cylinders shown in Fig. 50 are equal in diameter and have weights as indicated. Determine the pressures at A, B, C, and D.

Ans. $A = 1880$ lb.; $B = 684$ lb.; $C = 1100$ lb.; $D = 1020$ lb.

3. A 200-lb. weight is supported by a system of cords as shown in Fig. 51. Determine the tension in each cord.

Ans. $T_1 = 104$ lb.; $T_2 = 146$ lb.; $T_3 = 51$ lb.; $T_4 = 128$ lb.

FIG. 51.

FIG. 52.

4. Determine the forces exerted by the members AB and BC of the simple frame shown in Fig. 52.

Ans. $AB = 4800$ lb. compression; $BC = 6000$ lb. tension.

5. Solve Prob. 4 if the 3600-lb. load is directed downward to the left at 30° with the vertical.

Ans. $AB = 5960$ lb. compression; $BC = 5200$ lb. tension.

6. The three cylinders in Fig. 53 are equal in diameter and have weights as indicated. Determine the pressures at A, B, C, and D.

Ans. $A = 231$ lb.; $B = 1000$ lb.; $C = 1430$ lb.; $D = 327$ lb.

FIG. 53.

7. What horizontally applied force P will be required to start the 300-lb. block in Fig. 54 down the slope assuming the surface of the slope to be smooth? What is the normal pressure between block and incline?

Ans. $P = 57.7$ lb.; $N = 231$ lb.

Fig. 54.   Fig. 55.

8. Determine the forces exerted by the members AB and BC of the frame shown in Fig. 55. *Ans.* $AB = 1250$ lb. compression; $BC = 938$ lb. tension.

Art. 15. Parallel Forces in Equilibrium.

Either algebraic or graphic methods may be applied in the solution of problems involving parallel forces in equilibrium. The conditions of equilibrium, $\Sigma F = 0$ and $\Sigma M = 0$, are used in the algebraic method. Since only two independent equations are possible, there must be no more than two unknowns. In the graphic method, the principle of inverse proportion explained in Art. 6 may be applied.

Example

A beam 30 ft. long weighing 50 lb. per ft. is supported at the right end and at 5 ft. from the left end. It carries a uniformly distributed load of 200 lb. per ft. over a length of 10 ft. from the right end and a concentrated load of 750 lb. at 10 ft. from the left end. Compute the reactions at the supports.

Fig. 56.

Solution: Algebraic Method. The beam is shown as a free body in Fig. 56. If moments are taken about point B, the reaction R_2 is eliminated and the resulting equation contains only one unknown. Since a uniformly distributed load is a set of parallel forces located at equal distances apart, the resultant of such load acts at the center of distribution and the moment may be obtained as the product of the total load and the distance of the center of distribution from the moment center. Thus

$$\Sigma M_B = 25\,R_1 - 750 \times 20 - (50 \times 30) \times 15 - (200 \times 10) \times 5 = 0$$
$$R_1 = 1900\ \text{lb.}$$

In similar manner, moments are taken about A.

$$\Sigma M_A = 25\,R_2 - 750 \times 5 - (50 \times 30) \times 10 - (200 \times 10) \times 20 = 0$$
$$R_2 = 2350\ \text{lb.}$$

The equation, $\Sigma F_V = 0$, may be used as a check:

$$\Sigma F_V = 1900 + 2350 - 750 - (50 \times 30) - (200 \times 10) = 0$$
$$4250 - 4250 = 0$$

Graphic Method.   Fig. 57 shows the beam laid out with all distances measured to scale.   The resultant of the 750- and 1500-lb. loads is

Fig. 57.

2250 lb., whose location is obtained by the inverse proportion method. The beam itself is used as the base line; the 750-lb. force is laid off to scale above the base line on the action line of the 1500-lb. force.   The 1500 lb. is laid off to scale below the base line on the action line of the 750-lb. force. The connecting diagonal is drawn, its intersection with the base line locating the 2250-lb. resultant.   The resultant of the latter and the remaining 2000-lb. load is 4250 lb., whose location is likewise determined by the inverse proportion method as shown in the diagram.

The resultant of all the loads which has just been determined is now resolved by the inverse proportion principle into two components acting at A and B.   To do this, the value 4250 is laid off to scale from A to H on the line of action of the reaction R_1.   The line HB then divides the resultant load at K into two components which scale 1900 lb. and 2350 lb.

and act at A and B respectively.   The reactions R_1 and R_2 must be equal and opposite to the corresponding load components.

An alternative graphic method is available involving the use of the funicular polygon.   A discussion of the procedure involved may be found in textbooks dealing more fully with graphic methods.

Problems

1. Determine the reactions R_1 and R_2 of the beam shown in Fig. 58.

Ans. $R_1 = 3875$ lb.; $R_2 = 3125$ lb.

FIG. 58.   FIG. 59.

2. Determine the reactions at the supports A and B of the roof truss shown in Fig. 59.   Ans. $R_A = 4500$ lb.; $R_B = 5000$ lb.

3. Compute the reactions at the supports A and B of the beam shown in Fig. 60.   Ans. $R_A = 10,400$ lb.; $R_B = 5800$ lb.

FIG. 60.   FIG. 61.

4. Solve for the reactions R_1 and R_2 of the beam shown in Fig. 61.

Ans. $R_1 = 1290$ lb.; $R_2 = 1140$ lb.

FIG. 62.

5. Solve for the reactions R_1 and R_2 of the beam in Fig. 62.

Ans. $R_1 = 4350$ lb.; $R_2 = 3050$ lb.

Art. 16. Non-concurrent, Non-parallel Forces in Equilibrium. Both algebraic and graphic methods of solution will be considered in the solution of this type of problem. In the algebraic method the conditions of equilibrium, $\Sigma F_x = 0$, $\Sigma F_y = 0$, and $\Sigma M = 0$, are used. By a proper selection of moment centers and directions of resolution, all but one of the unknowns may usually be eliminated from a given equation and thus simultaneous equations are avoided. Since it is possible to set up three independent equations, such a system of forces may involve as many as three unknowns and remain statically determinate.

The graphic method of solution usually consists in combining all known forces into their resultant so as to reduce the system to three forces, if possible. These three, if not parallel, must be concurrent, and the solution is completed by the methods of Art. 14. When the system cannot be reduced to three forces, other schemes are available. It is left to the ingenuity of the student particularly interested in graphic methods to develop the necessary means.

Example 1

The arm ABC in Fig. 63 (a) is pinned to the wall at A and supported at C by the cable CD. Compute the tension in the cable and the pin reaction at A when the arm carries a 400-lb. load at B.

Fig. 63.

Solution: The arm ABC is selected as a free body as shown in Fig. 63 (b). The reaction at A is unknown in both magnitude and direction. Although the direction of this reaction could be determined by using the principle of concurrence of three forces, it is often convenient to replace such an unknown by its rectangular components. So, in this example, R_A has been replaced by vertical and horizontal components, A_V and A_H. By taking moments about A, both of these unknowns are eliminated, thus

$$\Sigma M_A = 400 \times 6 - CD \times (10 \sin 30°) = 0$$

$$2400 - CD(-5) = 0$$

$$2400 - 2400 = 0 \qquad CD = 480$$

from which $CD = 480$ lb. tension. Then

$$\Sigma F_V = A_V + 480 \sin 30° - 400 = 0$$

$$A_V = 160 \text{ lb.}$$

and $$\Sigma F_H = A_H - 480 \cos 30° = 0$$

$$A_H = 416 \text{ lb.}$$

The total reaction at A, shown in Fig. 63 (c), may be completely determined from its components:

$$R_A = \sqrt{(160)^2 + (416)^2} = 446 \text{ lb.}$$

$$\theta_H = \tan^{-1} \frac{160}{416} = 21°$$

The above example may be solved by alternative methods. For instance, the intersection of the 400-lb. force and the cable tension determines the line of action of the pin reaction R_A. This intersection may be located and the solution completed graphically, or the intersection may be located by trigonometric methods, the angle θ_H determined, and the solution completed by either trigonometric or algebraic methods. It is left to the student to follow out these suggested alternatives.

Example 2

The tensions in the two sides of a belt driving the windlass in Fig. 64 are 350 lb. and 150 lb. Solve for the resistance W that can be overcome, and for the magnitude and direction of the bearing pressure at A.

FIG. 64.

Solution: Algebraic Method. The unknown bearing reaction at A is represented by its components A_V and A_H as shown in Fig. 64. These two unknowns may be eliminated by moments about A.

$$\Sigma M_A = W \times \tfrac{1}{2} + 150 \times 1\tfrac{1}{2} - 350 \times 1\tfrac{1}{2} = 0 \qquad W = 600 \text{ lb.}$$

Then

$$\Sigma F_V = A_V - 600 \cos 15° + 150 \sin 30° = 0 \qquad A_V = 505 \text{ lb.}$$

$$\Sigma F_H = A_H - 600 \sin 15° - 150 \cos 30° - 350 = 0 \quad A_H = 635 \text{ lb.}$$

The resultant bearing pressure may now be found from its components.

$$R_A = \sqrt{(635)^2 + (505)^2} = 810 \text{ lb.}$$

$$\theta_H = \tan^{-1} \frac{505}{635} = 38.5°$$

Graphic Method. The windlass itself must first be laid out to scale as shown in Fig. 65. The number of forces is reduced to three by com-

Fig. 65.

bining the two known belt pulls into their resultant, $T' = 485$ lb., by the parallelogram law. The free body is now acted upon by a system of three forces, T', W, and the bearing reaction R_A. Since these forces are not parallel, they must be concurrent as explained in Art. 12. The forces T' and W are therefore extended to their intersection K. The bearing reaction R_A must also pass through this point, thus determining its line of action and the angle θ_H which scales 38.5°. Starting with the known value of T', the force triangle consisting of T', W, and R_A is constructed as shown, from which W scales 600 lb. and R_A scales 810 lb.

Problems

1. Solve for the tension BD and the V and H components of the pin reaction at A in Fig. 66.

Ans. $BD = 6000$ lb. T; $A_H = 5200$ lb.; $A_V = 1000$ lb.

FIG. 66.   FIG. 67.

2. Determine the tension in AB and the V and H components of the pin reaction at C, in the crane, Fig. 67.

Ans. $AB = 6790$ lb. T; $C_H = 4800$ lb.; $C_V = 7200$ lb.

3. The block in Fig. 68 weighs 800 lb. and is held in a horizontal position by the force P and hinge A. Solve for P and the resultant hinge reaction.

Ans. $P = 375$ lb.; $R_A = 510$ lb.; $\theta_H = 111.5°$.

FIG. 68.   FIG. 69.

4. A steam hoist is shown in Fig. 69. When the crank pin B is 45° from dead center as shown, determine the tension in the connecting rod BC, and the V and H components of the bearing reaction at A. Assuming that the cross head C moves between smooth guides, determine the reaction of the guide upon the cross head and the steam pressure P.

Ans. $A_V = 6480$ lb.; $A_H = 1640$ lb.; $BC = 1710$ lb. T; $C_V = 483$ lb.; $P = 1640$ lb.

5. A ladder 20 ft. long and weighing 120 lb. rests against a smooth vertical wall at A and a smooth floor at B as shown in Fig. 70. A block fastened to the floor at B prevents slipping. Solve for the reactions at A and B when the ladder carries an additional load of 150 lb. at 5 ft. from B.

Ans. $A_H = 56.2$ lb.; $B_V = 270$ lb.; $B_H = 56.2$ lb.

Fig. 70. Fig. 71.

6. The roof truss in Fig. 71 rests on a roller at A and is supported by a hinge at B. Solve for the V and H components of the reactions at A and B.

Ans. $A_V = 8300$ lb.; $A_H = 0$; $B_V = 7160$ lb.; $B_H = 2000$ lb.

Supplementary Problems

1. Solve for the force P applied to the bell crank in Fig. 72 to overcome the 350-lb. resistance. Determine the amount and direction of the bearing reaction at B.

Ans. $P = 364$ lb.; $R_B = 660$ lb.; $\theta_H = 67.1°$.

2. Determine the compression in the brace BD and the V and H components of the pin reaction C in the crane, Fig. 73.

Ans. $BD = 1560$ lb.; $C_V = 750$ lb.; $C_H = 780$ lb.

Fig. 72. Fig. 73.

3. Assuming $T_2 = 2T_1$, solve for the belt pulls required to overcome resistance $P = 1200$ lb. when the water pump of Fig. 74 is in the position shown. The friction on the bearing at A and on the cross head C is to be considered negligible.   *Ans.* $T_2 = 1600$ lb.

Fig. 74.   Fig. 75.

4. The cantilever truss in Fig. 75 is supported by a hinge at A and a brace CD. Solve for the compression in the brace and the components of the hinge reaction.   *Ans.* $CD = 5500$ lb.; $A_V = 3750$ lb.; $A_H = 4760$ lb.

5. A 30-ft. ladder weighing 50 lb. rests on a smooth floor at A and against a smooth wall at B as shown in Fig. 76. A tie rod CD keeps the ladder from slipping. Solve for tension CD and reactions at A and B.

Ans. $CD = 28.1$ lb.; $A_V = 50$ lb.; $B_H = 28.1$ lb.

Fig. 76.   Fig. 77.

6. Two cylinders are placed as shown in Fig. 77. Compute the reactions at A, B, C, and D.

Ans. $A = 1060$ lb.; $B = 1380$ lb.; $C = 1250$ lb.; $D = 786$ lb.

7. Solve for the reactions at A and B for the cylinders shown in Fig. 78.

Ans. $A = 13.3$ lb.; $B = 33.3$ lb.

FIG. 78.   FIG. 79.

8. Fig. 79 represents the forces acting at a joint in a roof truss. Compute the values of P and Q for equilibrium. *Ans.* $P = 13,100$ lb. T; $Q = 6550$ lb. C.

9. Determine the reactions of the beam shown in Fig. 80.

Ans. $R_1 = 1500$ lb.; $R_2 = 2500$ lb.

FIG. 80.   FIG. 81.

10. Compute the least force P to start the wheel of Fig. 81 over the block.

Ans. $P = 130$ lb.

CHAPTER III

STRESSES AND REACTIONS IN SIMPLE STRUCTURES

Art. 17. Two-force Members. When forces are applied at
only *two points* on a member, the system may be reduced to two
resultant forces and the member is known as a *two-force* member.
For equilibrium, the resultant of the forces at one of these points
must be equal, opposite, and collinear with the resultant of the
forces at the other point. Thus the force or stress in the member
must be directed along the axis connecting the two points, and it
is known as an axial stress. Such a stress action will be either tension or compression. In frames or structures containing two-force
members it is possible to cut through such members in selecting a
free body because the internal forces thus exposed are known to
be axial in direction with respect to the respective members
through which a section has been made.

A truss is a structure composed of members joined together to
form triangles as shown in Fig. 82. If it is assumed that the

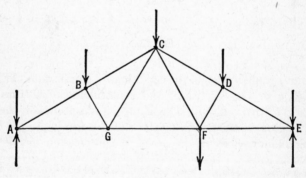

Fig. 82.

weights of the members are negligible in comparison with the loads
carried, that the loads are applied only at the joints, and that the
members are connected by pins with no member extending beyond

the joints at its ends, it becomes evident that each member will be a two-force member as described above.

In most trusses the members are riveted together at the joints and some members may extend continuously through several joints. There will be some bending action on the member resulting from such construction, thus making the stress more complex. However, in analyzing such trusses, it is customary to treat them as if pin-connected. In the following articles all trusses are to be considered as pin-connected at the joints.

Art. 18. Internal Stresses in Trusses; Method of Joints. The stresses in the various members of a truss may be determined by taking successive joints as free bodies. If all members in the truss are two-force members, then each joint when taken as a free body is acted upon by a system of concurrent forces in equilibrium as shown in Fig. 83. Two unknown forces may be determined for

Fig. 83.

each joint by application of the conditions of equilibrium, $\Sigma F_x = 0$ and $\Sigma F_y = 0$. In the design and construction of a truss it is necessary to make a compression member considerably heavier than a tension member carrying the same load owing to the buckling or column effect taking place in compression members of appreciable length. Hence, in stating the stress in a given member, the nature of the stress, tension or compression, should be given as well as the magnitude. The stress may be indicated by the letters at the joints which it connects. Thus, the stress in the member connecting joints A and B is known as AB.

Example

Solve for the stress in each member in the left half of the roof truss shown in Fig. 84.

Fig. 84.

Solution: The reaction R_1 is first obtained, the entire truss being the free body.

$$\Sigma M_G = 30\,R_1 - 8000 \times 15 - 3000 \times 10 = 0 \quad R_1 = 5000 \text{ lb.}$$

The joint A is now taken as a free body, and is shown in Fig. 85. It is acted upon by four concurrent forces of which two are known and two, AB and AC, are unknown in magnitude only. The directions of AB and AC are easily determined by inspection.

$$\Sigma F_y = AB \sin 30° + 1000 - 5000 = 0$$

Fig. 85.   gives $AB = 8000$ lb. C.

The direction of AB in Fig. 85 shows that it is pressing against the joint and is therefore compression.

$$\Sigma F_x = AC - 8000 \cos 30° = 0$$

gives $AC = 6930$ lb. T. The direction of AC in the figure shows that it is tension.

The joint B is taken as the next free body, shown in Fig. 86. The stress AB, determined from the preceding free body, becomes a known force on joint B. Being a compressive stress, it must press against B as shown.

Fig. 86.

$$\Sigma F_x = BD + 2000 \sin 30° - 8000 = 0$$
$$BD = 7000 \text{ lb. } C$$
$$\Sigma F_y = BC - 2000 \cos 30° = 0$$
$$BC = 1732 \text{ lb. } C$$

The joint C is now taken as a free body as shown in Fig. 87.

$$\Sigma F_y = CD \sin 60° - 1732 \sin 60° = 0$$
$$CD = 1732 \text{ lb. } T$$

$$\Sigma F_x = CE + 1732 \cos 60° + 1732 \cos 60° - 6930 = 0$$
$$CE = 5198 \text{ lb. } T$$

The stresses in the remaining members of the truss may be obtained in a similar manner. If, in the analysis of a joint, the direction of an unknown stress is not evident by inspection, the stress may be assumed as either tension or compression. In the subsequent solution for this stress, a positive result will indicate the assumed direction to be correct; a negative result will indicate the assumed direction to be wrong.

FIG. 87.

Problems

1. Solve for the stress in each member of the truss shown in Fig. 88.

FIG. 88.

Ans. $AB = BD = 1200$ lb. C; $AC = CD = 1340$ lb. T;
$BC = 1200$ lb. C.

2. Determine the stress in each member of the truss shown in Fig. 89.

FIG. 89.

Ans. $AB = 14{,}100$ lb. C; $AC = 10{,}000$ lb. T;
$BC = 5660$ lb. T; $BD = 14{,}000$ lb. C;
$CD = 8480$ lb. T; $CE = 8000$ lb. T;
$DE = 11{,}300$ lb. C.

3. The truss in Fig. 90 is supported vertically at A and both horizontally and vertically at G. Determine the reactions and the internal stresses.

FIG. 90.

Ans. $R_1 = 2390$ lb.; $R_2 = 2690$ lb.; $R_3 = 1200$ lb.;
$AB = 3740$ lb. C; $AC = 2940$ lb. T; $BC = 1200$ lb. C;
$BD = 3740$ lb. C; $CD = 1200$ lb. T; $CE = 1730$ lb. T;
$DE = 3460$ lb.T; $DF = FG = 5380$ lb. C; $EF = 0$; $EG = 3460$ lb. T.

4. In the cantilever truss shown in Fig. 91 the reaction at A is horizontal since the link AB is a two-force member. Determine this reaction, the amount and direction of the reaction at C, and the internal stresses.

FIG. 91.

Ans. $R_C = 3960$ lb.; $\theta_H = 49°$; $AB = 2600$ lb. T; $BC = 1500$ lb. C.;
$BD = 1300$ lb. T; $BE = 1500$ lb. T; $CE = 3000$ lb. C;
$DE = 1500$ lb. C; $DF = 1300$ lb. T; $EF = 1500$ lb. C.

5. Solve for the internal stresses in the truss shown in Fig. 92.

FIG. 92.

Ans. $AB = 10,000$ lb. C; $AC = 12,500$ lb. T; $BC = 7500$ lb. C;
$BD = 13,300$ lb. C; $BE = 4170$ lb. T; $CE = 10,000$ lb. T;
$DE = 5000$ lb. C.

Art. 19. Internal Stresses in Trusses; Method of Sections.

The stress in any designated member of a truss may sometimes be determined more advantageously by passing a section through the truss cutting the member in question and then considering as a free body the entire part of the truss lying on either side of the section. If the stresses in only a few members of a truss are required, this method is shorter than the method of joints.

Example 1

Solve for the stresses in members DF and DE of the truss shown in Fig. 93.

FIG. 93.

Solution: The reactions may be found by moments, using the entire truss as the free body.

$$\Sigma M_I = 120\,R_1 - 10,000 \times 90 - 10,000 \times 60 - 40,000 \times 30 = 0$$
$$R_1 = 22,500 \text{ lb.}$$

FIG. 94.

The section y–y is now passed through the truss and the portion of the truss on the left of this section is selected as the free body, as shown in Fig. 94. Three unknown forces appear, but since the system is non-concurrent, a solution can be made. The unknown stress DF may be obtained by applying $\Sigma M_E = 0$.

$$DF \times 20 + 10,000 \times 30 - 22,500 \times 60 = 0$$
$$DF = 52,500 \text{ lb. } C$$

The unknown stress DE may be found by applying $\Sigma F_V = 0$.

$$DE \times \tfrac{20}{25} + 10,000 - 22,500 = 0$$
$$DE = 15,600 \text{ lb. } T$$

In order to obtain these same stresses by the method of joints it would be necessary to solve successively the joints at *A*, *B*, *C*, and *D*.

The method of sections is also useful if the method of joints is inadequate to complete the solution; an example follows.

Example 2

Solve for the internal stresses in the truss shown in Fig. 95.

FIG. 95.

Solution: By symmetry, the reactions R_1 and R_2 are seen to be 16,000 lb. each. The internal stresses in members intersecting at joints

FIG. 96.

A, *B*, and *C* may be found by the method of joints. However, each of the adjacent joints *D* and *E* involves three unknowns and since the system of forces for each joint is concurrent, a solution cannot be made and it becomes impossible to proceed further by this method. A section *y–y* is now passed through the truss, and the part of the truss lying on the left of the section is selected as the free body as shown in Fig. 96. There are three unknown forces, but since the system is non-concurrent, the unknowns may be determined. The condition of equilibrium $\Sigma M_H = 0$ is applied.

$$EL \times 17.32 + 16,000 \times 15 - 16,000 \times 30 = 0$$
$$EL = 13,900 \text{ lb. } T$$

Since the stress *EL* is known, the joint *E* involves only two unknowns and may be solved; the remainder of the internal stresses may now be obtained by the method of joints or by the method of sections.

Problems

1. Solve for the stresses in members BC, CG, and GF of the truss shown in Fig. 97.

    Ans. $BC = 5800$ lb. C; $CG = 1730$ lb. T; $GF = 4160$ lb. T.

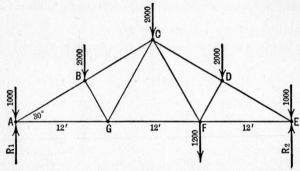

Fig. 97.

2. Solve for the stresses in members AC, BC, BD, and CD of the truss in Fig. 98.   *Ans.* $AC = 19,200$ lb. T; $BC = 10,100$ lb. C;
    $BD = 13,600$ lb. C; $CD = 8400$ lb. T.

Fig. 98.

3. Determine the stress in members BC, CG, and GF of the truss in Fig. 99.

Fig. 99.

    Ans. $BC = 14,400$ lb. T; $CG = 27,400$ lb. C; $GF = 721$ lb. C.

4. Solve for the stresses BD, CD, and CE of the truss in Fig.100.

Ans. $BD = 3460$ lb. T; $CD = 0$; $CE = 6920$ lb. C.

Fig. 100.

5. Each of the loads acting on the truss in Fig. 101 is 20,000 lb.   Determine the stresses in members a, b, c, d, and e.

Ans. $a = 112,500$ lb. C; $b = 12,500$ lb. C; $c = 120,000$ lb. T;
$d = 20,000$ lb. T; $e = 70,000$ lb. T.

Fig. 101.

6. Determine the stresses in members a, b, and c of the truss in Fig. 102.

Ans. $a = 19,000$ lb. C; $b = 12,100$ lb. T; $c = 10,400$ lb. T.

Fig. 102.

Art. 20. Bow's Notation. In the graphic method of determining internal stresses in a truss, a lettering scheme known as Bow's notation is of considerable advantage. In this method of notation, spaces are lettered rather than joints, and a force or stress is then denoted by the letters of the spaces which it separates. In Fig. 103 is shown a truss lettered according to this scheme. In lettering the spaces they are taken in order in the clockwise direc-

FIG. 103.

tion. In designating the forces acting upon a given joint, the letters are also taken in a clockwise direction. Thus, the joint at the left end of the truss is acted upon by four forces which will be referred to as follows. The reaction R_1, separating spaces h and a, is known as HA; the 500-lb. load becomes AB; the remaining unknown stresses are BI and IH.

Art. 21. Internal Stresses in Trusses;   Graphic Method. The physical dimensions of many trusses are such that algebraic methods of solving for internal stresses are very cumbersome and laborious; the graphic method of analysis may be shorter and easier. The use of Bow's notation facilitates the graphic solution. The steps involved are as follows:

(1) The truss is drawn completely to some convenient scale. This is known as the space diagram.

(2) All loads are combined graphically into a single resultant by methods explained in Chap. I. The constructions required may be superimposed on the space diagram.

(3) Since the resultant load and the reactions are in equilibrium, a graphic construction according to methods explained in Chap. II may be made to obtain the reactions. This construction likewise is made on the space diagram.

(4) As a separate figure, the equilibrium polygon, consisting of external loads and reactions on the entire truss as a free body, is laid out to scale. This will be known as the external load line.

(5) The method of joints is now applied to the joint at one end of the truss, the equilibrium polygon of the forces acting on this joint being constructed. Since certain forces involved in this polygon form part of the load line, the polygon is attached directly to the load line.

(6) In a similar manner polygons for the remaining joints are constructed in succession. The completed figure consisting of load line and the connected force polygons for the joints is called the force diagram.

(7) Magnitudes of the unknown stresses are scaled off directly from the force diagram.

(8) The character of each stress, tension or compression, is determined by the direction of the stress in the force diagram, taking the order of letters in clockwise direction around the joint on which the stress is considered to act.

Example

By the graphic method, solve for the reactions and stresses in the truss shown in Fig. 103.

Solution: The truss is laid out to scale and lettered, using Bow's notation, as shown in Fig. 104 (a).

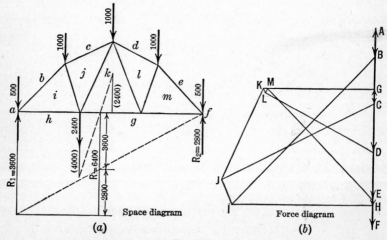

FIG. 104.

The loads on the truss are combined graphically, by the method of inverse proportion, into their resultant, 6400 lb., which is then resolved by the same principle into components equal and opposite to R_1 and R_2 which scale 3600 lb. and 2800 lb. respectively.

The external load line is now constructed, starting with force AB and closing with force HA, as shown in Fig. 104 (b). The polygon A–B–I–H–A of the forces acting on the joint at the left end of the truss is constructed, from which the magnitudes of the unknown stresses BI and IH are found to scale 4380 lb. and 3100 lb. respectively. Since spaces around a joint are taken in clockwise order, the stress in the member separating spaces b and i is known as BI. In the force diagram, the direction B to I shows the way in which the stress is acting on the joint under consideration. The direction is downward to the left, showing that member bi is pushing on the joint and thus the stress BI is compression. Similarly IH acts to the right on the joint and is therefore tension.

The force polygons for the remaining joints are then laid out to form the complete force diagram. Thus $IJ = 580$ lb. C; $JK = 2100$ lb. T; $MG = 2300$ lb. T; etc.

If all constructions are accurately made, the final force polygon will close. A failure of the last polygon to close indicates some error in construction. The process thus becomes self-checking.

Problems

1. Determine by the graphic method the reactions and internal stresses in the truss shown in Fig. 105. The support at the left end is to take all of the horizontal thrust. Force H–I is 8000 lb.

Fig. 105.

Ans. $IA = 16,900$ lb.; $GH = 17,600$ lb.; $BJ = 17,700$ lb. C;
$CK = 17,200$ lb. C; $EL = 16,900$ lb. C; $JI = 6200$ lb. T;
$JK = 8700$ lb. T; $LH = 8700$ lb. T; $KL = 4600$ lb. T.

2. Using the graphic method, solve for the reactions and stresses in the truss, Fig. 106. The support at the right end is assumed to take all the horizontal thrust.

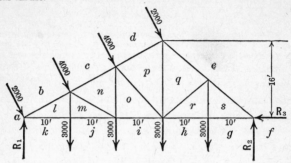

Fig. 106.

Ans. R_1 = 12,500 lb.; BL = 22,900 lb. C; LK = 19,300 lb. T;
NO = 6800 lb. T; EQ = 13,800 lb. C.

3. Solve graphically for the reactions and stresses in the truss shown in Fig. 107.

Fig. 107.

Ans. GH = 19,900 lb. C; BI = 3450 lb. T; KL = 4800 lb. C;
NF = 3700 lb. C.

Art. 22. Three-force Members. When forces are applied at more than two points on a member, the system cannot be reduced to two forces as was done with the two-force member in Art. 17, and the member is known as a *three-force member.* It is not necessary now that the resultant stress action be directed along the axis of the member. In general, the stress action is more complex, involving bending and shear. No attempt will be made here to investigate further the stresses in such members, but the reactions exerted where they are joined to other members may be determined. Since the direction and nature of the stress action in a three-force member are unknown, a section should not be taken through a member of this type in selecting a free body; hence the free body must contain the entire member. In analyzing structures or frames containing three-force members, it will usually be necessary to use the entire frame as the first free body for the purpose of determining unknown external reactions. Individual members are then taken out as successive free bodies in order to determine the pin reactions at joints.

Example 1

The A-frame shown in Fig. 108 rests on a smooth floor at A and F. Solve for the external reactions at these points and for the pin reactions at B, C, and D.

Solution: Each of the three members of the frame is acted upon by forces at more than two points and is therefore a three-force member.

FIG. 108.

Since the frame rests on a smooth surface, the reactions at A and F are normal to the surface. With the entire frame as the first free body, Fig. 108, these reactions are determined.

$$\Sigma M_F = 20R_A - 1200 \times 2 = 0 \qquad\qquad R_A = 120 \text{ lb.}$$

Either

$$\Sigma F_V = 0 \quad \text{or} \quad \Sigma M_A = 0 \quad \text{gives} \quad R_F = 1320 \text{ lb.}$$

The cross bar BDE is the next free body as shown in Fig. 109 (a). The reactions at B and D, unknown in both magnitude and direction, are represented by means of their vertical and horizontal components.

There are thus four unknowns so that a complete solution cannot be made. The following results may be obtained however:

$$\Sigma M_D = 12 B_V - 1200 \times 6 = 0 \qquad B_V = 600 \text{ lb.}$$
$$\Sigma F_V = 0 \quad \text{or} \quad \Sigma M_B = 0 \quad \text{then gives} \quad D_V = 1800 \text{ lb.}$$
$$\Sigma F_H = B_H - D_H = 0 \qquad B_H = D_H$$

Either one of the diagonal members may now be taken as a free body. The member ABC is shown in Fig. 109 (b); since R_A and B_V have already

(a)

(b)

FIG. 109.

been determined, only three unknowns remain and the solution may be completed.

$$\Sigma M_C = 6B_H + 120 \times 10 - 600 \times 6 = 0 \qquad B_H = 400 \text{ lb.} = D_H$$
$$\Sigma F_V = C_V - 600 + 120 = 0 \qquad C_V = 480 \text{ lb.}$$
$$\Sigma F_H = C_H - 400 = 0 \qquad C_H = 400 \text{ lb.}$$

The magnitude and direction of the total pin reactions may be determined, if desired, by combining the H and V components.

Example 2

Solve for the components of the pin reactions at A and D and the stresses in members BE and CF of the frame shown in Fig. 110 (a).

Solution: In this frame, the members ABC and DEF are three-force members; members BE and CF are two-force members in which the stress is axial.

The entire frame is the first free body, shown in Fig. 110 (a). Since the directions of the pin reactions at A and D are unknown, they are represented by their V and H components. Since there are four unknowns, only a partial solution is possible. The conditions of equilibrium are applied as follows:

$$\Sigma M_D = 3A_H - 1500 \times 12 = 0 \qquad A_H = 6000 \text{ lb.}$$
$$\Sigma F_H = 0 \quad \text{or} \quad \Sigma M_A = 0 \quad \text{then gives} \quad D_H = 6000 \text{ lb.}$$
$$\Sigma F_V = D_V - A_V - 1500 = 0 \qquad A_V = D_V - 1500$$

FIG. 110.

Either one of the two three-force members may be selected as the next free body. Let member DEF be chosen, as shown in Fig. 110 (b). There are but three unknowns, and the solution may be completed by the following equations.

$$\Sigma M_O = 10D_V - 6000 \times 5 = 0 \qquad D_V = 3000 \text{ lb.}$$
$$\Sigma F_H = BE \cos 45° - 6000 = 0 \qquad BE = 8484 \text{ lb. } C$$
$$\Sigma M_E = 5CF - 3000 \times 5 = 0 \qquad CF = 3000 \text{ lb. } T$$

Since $\quad A_V = D_V - 1500 \qquad A_V = 1500 \text{ lb.}$

Problems

1. Assume the reactions at A and E of the A-frame in Fig. 111 to be vertical. Solve for these reactions and the components of the pin reactions at B, C, and D.   *Ans.* $R_A = 1000$ lb.; $R_E = 2000$ lb.; $B_V = 750$ lb.; $B_H = 375$ lb.; $C_V = 250$ lb.; $C_H = 375$ lb.; $D_V = 2250$ lb.; $D_H = 375$ lb.

FIG. 111.   FIG. 112.

2. In the crane shown in Fig. 112, the reaction at D is horizontal. Deter-

mine this reaction, the components of the reactions at A and C, and the stress in member BE.

Ans. $D_H = A_H = 2000$ lb.; $A_V = 2400$ lb.;
$C_V = 600$ lb.; $C_H = 4000$ lb.; $BE = 5000$ lb. C.

3. Solve for the components of the reactions at A, B, C, D, and E of the crane in Fig. 112 if each member weighs 50 lb. per ft.

Ans. $A_V = 4000$ lb.; $A_H = D_H = 2375$ lb.;
$B_H = C_H = E_H = 4750$ lb.; $B_V = 3810$ lb.; $C_V = 413$ lb.;
$E_V = 3310$ lb.

4. Solve for the reactions at A and C and the stresses in members BD and BE of the cantilever frame in Fig. 113.

Ans. $A_H = C_H = 2400$ lb.; $A_V = 160$ lb.; $C_V = 960$ lb.;
$BD = 4000$ lb. C; $BE = 2240$ lb. T.

FIG. 113.   FIG. 114.

5. The reaction at B on the crane shown in Fig. 114 is horizontal. Solve for this reaction, the components of the reactions at A and E, and the stress in member CD.

Ans. $B_H = A_H = 4000$ lb.; $A_V = 2000$ lb.; $E_V = 6000$ lb.;
$E_H = 4000$ lb.; $CD = 5660$ lb. T.

6. The frame shown in Fig. 115 rests on a smooth floor at F. Solve for

FIG. 115.

the reactions at E and F, and the amount and direction of the pin pressures at A, B, and D.

$Ans.$ $R_E = 30$ lb.; $R_F = 150$ lb.; $R_A = 152$ lb. at $23.2°$ with H;
$R_B = 228$ lb. at $52.1°$ with H; $R_D = 252$ lb. at $56.3°$ with H.

Art. 23. Redundant Members. When a structure consists of more members than are necessary for stability, it is said to be redundant and the members not required for stability are called redundant members. The truss shown in Fig. 116 furnishes an example of a redundant system. If a section m–n is taken through the truss, the resulting free body is acted upon by four unknown

FIG. 116.

stresses and the system is statically indeterminate. If the members a and b can carry either tension or compression, both are not needed to maintain stability of the truss and either one may be designated as a redundant member. However, if these members are of such character that they are capable of carrying tension only, such as cables or slender rods, only one of the two will be acting under a given condition of loading and the system is reduced to three unknowns, becoming statically determinate. If member b in Fig. 116 is removed, member a will be in compression. When member a is removed, b will be in tension. Therefore if these members are capable of carrying tension only, member b acts while a remains idle. Similarly, in the next panel, member c is not acting.

Problems

1. Assume that members BF and CE of the truss in Fig. 117 can carry tension only. Determine the stress in the one which is acting.

$$Ans. \; CE = 5000 \text{ lb. } T.$$

FIG. 117.

2. Assuming that the diagonal members of the truss in Fig. 118 can carry tension only, determine the stresses in those which are acting.

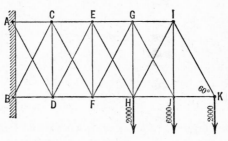

FIG. 118.

$$Ans. \; AD = CF = EH = 11{,}500 \text{ lb. } T; \; GJ = 9240 \text{ lb. } T;$$
$$IK = 2310 \text{ lb. } T.$$

Art. 24. Parabolic Cables. When a flexible cable or cord is suspended between two points of support and is subjected to a distributed loading, the cable will assume the form of a curve the exact shape of which is dependent on the nature of the distribution of the load. The case of load distributed uniformly horizontally will be considered first. The suspension bridge illustrated in Fig. 119 furnishes an example of this type of loading, provided that the floor of the bridge is loaded uniformly and that the vertical cables are spaced equal distance apart and relatively close to-

gether.   It will now be shown that under such loading conditions
the cable will take the shape of a parabola.

Fig. 119.

In Fig. 120 (*a*) is shown a cord suspended from points *A* and *B*
and loaded with a load, *w* pounds per foot, distributed uniformly
along the horizontal.   The horizontal distance *l*, between supports, is known as the span; and the distance *d*, from the level of
the supports to the lowest point *O* of the cord, is known as the

Fig. 120.

sag.   The portion of the cord included between *O* and any other
point *P* is taken as a free body, shown in Fig. 120 (*b*).   With *O* as
the origin of coordinate axes, the coordinates of point *P* are *x,y*.
The resultant load on this portion of the cord is *wx* acting midway
between *O* and *P* since the load is distributed uniformly horizontally.   Since *O* is the lowest point in the cord, the tangent here is
horizontal and the tension *H* at this point is horizontal.   The tension *T* in the cord at *P* must be concurrent with *H* and the load
wx as shown.   By moments about *P*:

$$H \cdot y - wx \cdot \frac{x}{2} = 0$$

or

$$y = \frac{w}{2H} \cdot x^2$$

This equation is of the form $y = ax^2 + bx + c$ and therefore represents a parabola with vertical axis.

The triangle of forces shown in Fig. 120 (c) shows that the tension T is greater than H and increases when x increases, so that the maximum tension T occurs at the points of support. At either A or B, x and y become $l/2$ and d, respectively, and the equation of moments becomes

$$Hd - \frac{wl}{2} \cdot \frac{l}{4} = 0$$

or

$$\mathbf{H} = \frac{\mathbf{wl^2}}{\mathbf{8d}}$$

From the triangle of forces,

$$\mathbf{T} = \sqrt{\mathbf{H^2} + \left(\frac{\mathbf{wl}}{\mathbf{2}}\right)^2}$$

$$\boldsymbol{\theta} = \tan^{-1}\frac{\mathbf{wl}}{\mathbf{2H}} = \tan^{-1}\frac{\mathbf{4d}}{\mathbf{l}}$$

The length s of the cord will next be determined. From the calculus, the length of any curve is given by

$$s = \int \left[1 + \left(\frac{dy}{dx}\right)^2\right]^{\frac{1}{2}} dx$$

By differentiation of $y = \dfrac{wx^2}{2H}$, the result $\dfrac{dy}{dx} = \dfrac{wx}{H}$ is obtained. If this result is substituted above,

$$s = 2\int_0^{\frac{l}{2}} \left[1 + \left(\frac{wx}{H}\right)^2\right]^{\frac{1}{2}} dx = 2\int_0^{\frac{l}{2}} \left[1 + \frac{64d^2x^2}{l^4}\right]^{\frac{1}{2}} dx$$

the exact expression for s from this integral is a logarithmic function and is cumbersome to use. A simple expression for s may be obtained by expanding the term in brackets into a converging series and integrating term by term, the following equation resulting,

$$\mathbf{s} = 1 + \frac{\mathbf{8d^2}}{\mathbf{31}} - \frac{\mathbf{32d^4}}{\mathbf{51^3}} + \cdots$$

The fourth and succeeding terms of the above series are so small that they may be neglected without appreciable error.

The case of load distributed uniformly along the length of the cord will next be considered. An example of this is a cord loaded only by its own weight. The loads on successive unit lengths of the cord are not spaced at equal horizontal distances in this case and the cord assumes the shape of a curve called the catenary. The equation of the catenary involves exponential functions and is much more complex than the equation of the parabola. In fact, many problems involving the catenary can be solved only by trial. If, however, the sag is small relative to the span, the loading approaches uniform distribution horizontally and the catenary curve approximates very closely a parabola. When the sag is not more than one-tenth of the span, the error involved in solving as if the load were distributed uniformly horizontally is negligible for most engineering purposes. In the problems of this article, the above conditions may be assumed.

Example 1

The floor of a suspension bridge is 400 ft. long and 20 ft. wide and is supported by a cable on each side having sag of 25 ft. The bridge carries a load of 100 lb. per sq. ft. of floor area. Solve for the tension at the middle, the tension at the ends, and the length of the cables.

Solution: The total load on one cable is

$$\frac{400 \times 20 \times 100}{2} = 400,000 \text{ lb. or } 1000 \text{ lb. per ft.}$$

Fig. 121.

One half of the cable is taken as a free body as shown in Fig. 121. By moments about the point of support A,

$$H \times 25 = 200,000 \times 100 \qquad H = 800,000 \text{ lb.}$$

From the triangle of forces,

$$T = \sqrt{(800,000)^2 + (200,000)^2} = 825,000 \text{ lb.}$$

$$\theta = \tan^{-1}\frac{200,000}{800,000} = 14°$$

The length of the cable is

$$s = 400 + \frac{8(25)^2}{3(400)} - \frac{32(25)^4}{5(400)^3} = 404.13 \text{ ft.}$$

Example 2

A cable can safely carry 3000 lb. tension. Its weight is 0.5 lb. per linear foot. If the allowable sag is 30 ft., what is the maximum spacing for the supports?

FIG. 122.

Solution: If it is assumed that the unknown span l is more than 10 times the sag, the condition of load distributed uniformly horizontally is approximated, and furthermore H is approximately equal to $T = 3000$. Half of the cable is shown as a free body in Fig. 122. By moments

$$3000 \times 30 - \frac{0.5l}{2} \cdot \frac{l}{4} = 0$$

$$l^2 = 1{,}440{,}000 \qquad \text{and} \qquad l = 1200 \text{ ft.}$$

The ratio of sag to span is now $30/1200 = 1/40$, and the initial assumption is justified.

Problems

1. A cable having a span of 400 ft. and a sag of 50 ft. carries a uniformly distributed load of 1200 lb. per horizontal foot. Solve for the maximum tension and the length of the cable.

Ans. $T = 537{,}000$ lb. at 26.5° with H; $s = 416$ ft.

2. Determine the maximum spacing of poles to carry a wire weighing 0.05 lb. per ft. if the allowable tension in the wire is 300 lb. and the allowable sag is 2 ft.   *Ans.* $l = 310$ ft.

3. If a wire weighing 0.2 lb. per ft. is stretched between points 100 ft. apart until the tension reaches 600 lb., what will be the resulting sag?

Ans. $d = 0.417$ ft.

4. A cable of a suspension bridge has a span of 800 ft. and a sag of 100 ft. If the allowable tension for the cable is 500,000 lb., what is the maximum allowable load in pounds per foot distributed uniformly horizontally?

Ans. $w = 560$ lb. per ft.

Art. 25. The Catenary.

It was stated in Art. 24 that a cable loaded uniformly along its length assumes the shape of a catenary curve and that when the ratio of span to sag is small the methods developed for the parabolic cable may be used to a close degree of approximation. Consideration will now be given to the case where the ratio of span to sag is too large to permit the use of the approximate method.

Let AQB, in Fig. 123 (a), represent a cable loaded with w pounds per foot distributed uniformly along its length, and suspended from points A and B on the same horizontal level and at distance l apart. Let Q represent the lowest point on the cable, P any other point, and s the distance along the cable from Q to P. This portion of the cable is shown as a free body in Fig. 123 (b), where H represents the horizontal tension at Q, T the tension at P,

w lbs. per ft.

(a) (b)

Fig. 123.

and ws the resultant of the vertical loads. The equilibrium triangle of forces for the free body is shown in Fig. 123 (c), from which

$$\tan \theta = \frac{ws}{H} = \frac{s}{c}$$

where $c = \dfrac{H}{w}$ is a constant. Let O, at distance c below Q, be taken as the origin of coordinates, as indicated in Fig. 123 (b).

$$\frac{dy}{dx} = \tan \theta = \frac{s}{c} \tag{1}$$

$$ds^2 = dx^2 + dy^2 \quad \text{or} \quad dy = \sqrt{(ds^2) - (dx)^2} \tag{2}$$

By eliminating dy from equations (1) and (2),

$$dx = \frac{c\,ds}{\sqrt{c^2 + s^2}}$$

or

$$\int_0^x dx = c \int_0^s \frac{ds}{\sqrt{c^2 + s^2}}$$

By integration

$$x = c \log_e \frac{s + \sqrt{c^2 + s^2}}{c} \tag{3}$$

Reducing to exponential form,

$$e^{\frac{x}{c}} = \frac{s + \sqrt{c^2 + s^2}}{c} \tag{4}$$

Solving for s,

$$s = \frac{c}{2}(e^{\frac{x}{c}} - e^{-\frac{x}{c}}) \tag{5}$$

By substitution of (5) in (1)

$$dy = \tfrac{1}{2}(e^{\frac{x}{c}} - e^{-\frac{x}{c}})dx \tag{6}$$

Let (6) be integrated over the portion of the curve from Q to P,

$$\int_c^y dy = \tfrac{1}{2}\int_0^x (e^{\frac{x}{c}} - e^{-\frac{x}{c}})dx$$

$$y - c = \frac{c}{2}(e^{\frac{x}{c}} + e^{-\frac{x}{c}}) - c$$

$$\mathbf{y = \frac{c}{2}(e^{\frac{x}{c}} + e^{-\frac{x}{c}})} \tag{7}$$

Equation (7) is the equation of the catenary curve in cartesian coordinates. By squaring (5) and (7) and subtracting,

$$\mathbf{y^2 = s^2 + c^2} \tag{8}$$

Substituting (8) in (3),

$$\mathbf{x = c \log_e \frac{s + y}{c}} \tag{9}$$

From Fig. 123 (b),

$$T^2 = w^2 s^2 + H^2 = w^2 s^2 + w^2 c^2 = w^2(s^2 + c^2)$$

$$\mathbf{T = w\sqrt{s^2 + c^2} = wy} \tag{10}$$

Equations (5) and (7) may also be written in terms of hyperbolic functions as follows:

$$\mathbf{s = \frac{c}{2}(e^{\frac{x}{c}} - e^{-\frac{x}{c}}) = c \sinh \frac{x}{c}} \tag{11}$$

$$\mathbf{y = \frac{c}{2}(e^{\frac{x}{c}} + e^{-\frac{x}{c}}) = c \cosh \frac{x}{c}} \tag{12}$$

In problems involving the catenary, the span l becomes $2x$ in the equations above, the length of the cable becomes $2s$, and the sag d becomes $y - c$. Owing to the form of the equations, many problems can be solved only by trial. A table of hyperbolic functions may facilitate the solution when equations (11) and (12) are used. *For any given tension there are two values of the sag that will produce that tension.*

Example

A cable weighing 4 lb. per ft. is suspended between two supports on the same level and 1000 ft. apart. The sag is 200 ft. Compute the maximum tension and the length of the cable.

Solution:

$$y = c + 200$$

From (8),

$$y^2 = s^2 + c^2 = c^2 + 400c + 40,000$$

$$s = \sqrt{400c + 40,000}$$

From (9),

$$x = 500 = c \log_e \frac{\sqrt{400c + 40,000} + (c + 200)}{c}$$

By trial it is found that the value $c = 660$ will very nearly satisfy this equation. Hence,

$$y = c + 200 = 860 \text{ ft.}$$

$$T = wy = 4 \times 860 = 3440 \text{ lb. at the supports.}$$

$$s = \sqrt{y^2 - c^2} = \sqrt{(860)^2 - (660)^2} = 550 \text{ ft.}$$

The length of cable, $2s = 1100$ ft.

Problems

1. Compute the span and sag of a cable 600 ft. long weighing 1 lb. per ft. and supported at points on the same level with a maximum tension of 800 lb.

Ans. 583 ft.; 59 ft.

2. A cable weighing 6 lb. per ft. is suspended between points 800 ft. apart on the same level. The sag is 200 ft. Compute the maximum tension and the length of the cable.

Ans. 3780 lb.; 918 ft.

3. A cable weighing 2 lb. per ft. is to be suspended between two supports on the same level, 600 ft. apart. If the maximum allowable tension in the cable is 1200 lb., determine the minimum sag to which the cable may be drawn up, and the length of the cable.   *Ans.* 92 ft.; 636 ft.

Supplementary Problems

1. Solve for the stresses in members AB, CD, CE, and FM of the truss in Fig. 124.

> *Ans.* $AB = 88,700$ lb. C; $CD = 37,800$ lb. T;
> $CE = 53,300$ lb. C; $FM = 133,000$ lb. T.

FIG. 124.

2. Solve for the reactions at A and H and stresses in members BD, BE and DE of the truss in Fig. 125.

> *Ans.* $A_V = 11,390$ lb.; $A_H = 0$; $H_V = 10,690$ lb.; $H_H = 1200$ lb.
> $BD = 11,050$ lb. C; $BE = 6390$ lb. C; $DE = 5700$ lb. T.

FIG. 125.

3. Solve for the reactions at A and D and the stresses in members BE and CE of the cantilever frame in Fig. 126.

FIG. 126.

> *Ans.* $A_H = D_H = 2500$ lb.; $A_V = 833$ lb.; $D_V = 333$ lb.;
> $BE = 2360$ lb. T; $CE = 1180$ lb. C.

4. The reaction at F on the frame shown in Fig. 127 is vertical. Determine the reaction at F and the V and H components of pin pressures at A, B, D, and E.

Ans. $R_F = 640$ lb.; $A_V = 640$ lb.; $A_H = 400$ lb.; $B_V = 640$ lb.;
$B_H = E_H = 200$ lb.; $D_V = E_V = 1280$ lb.; $D_H = 600$ lb.

FIG. 127.

FIG. 128. FIG. 129.

5. A cable carrying 40 lb. per horizontal foot is suspended from points A and B as shown in Fig. 128. Determine the tensions at A and B.

Ans. $T_A = 7610$ lb.; $T_B = 8310$ lb.

6. Assume that the diagonal braces below BC in the tower, Fig. 129, can carry tension only. Solve for all the internal stresses.

Ans. $AB = 1250$ lb. T; $AC = 1250$ lb. C; $BC = 750$ lb. C;
$BD = 1000$ lb. T; $CD = 2500$ lb. T; $DE = 1500$ lb. C; $CE = 3000$ lb. C;
$DF = 3000$ lb. T; $EF = 2500$ lb. T; $EG = 5000$ lb. C; $FG = 1500$ lb. C;
$FH = 5000$ lb. T; $GH = 2500$ lb. T; $GI = 7000$ lb. C.

7. The A-frame shown in Fig. 130 is mounted on wheels at A and E. Solve for reactions at A and E and the amount and direction of the pin pressures at B, C, and D.

Ans. $R_A = 375$ lb.; $R_E = 1875$ lb.; $R_B = 1530$ lb. at 100.6° with H;
$R_C = 1160$ lb. at 103.7° with H; $R_D = 3010$ lb. at 95.4° with H.

FIG. 130.

8. Solve for the stresses in members KL, KM, LM, and LN of the truss in Fig. 131.

Ans. $KL = 0$; $KM = 20,000$ lb. C; $LM = 0$; $LN = 16,000$ lb. T.

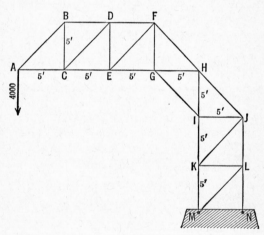

FIG. 131.

9. The frame shown in Fig. 132 is hinged at F and supported by a smooth surface at A. Compute the horizontal and vertical components of the pin reaction at C, and the stress in BE.

Ans. $C_H = 693$ lb.; $C_V = 800$ lb.; $BE = 693$ lb. T.

10. Let the 1200-lb. load shown in Fig. 132 act horizontally to the left. Solve for the pin reaction at C and the stress in BE.

$Ans.$ $C_H = 600$ lb.; $C_V = 1390$ lb.; $BE = 600$ lb. T.

FIG. 132. FIG. 133.

11. Determine the reactions at A and B, and the stresses in CE and CD for the structure shown in Fig. 133.

$Ans.$ $A_H = B_H = 1000$ lb.; $A_V = 1430$ lb.; $B_V = 570$ lb.; $CE = 1670$ lb. C; $CD = 763$ lb. T.

12. Place the load shown in Fig. 133 at point D, and for this position solve for all reactions and stresses.

$Ans.$ $B_H = 3500$ lb.; $B_V = 2000$ lb.; $AC = 3500$ lb. T; $CE = 5840$ lb. C; $CD = 4670$ lb. T.

13. Solve for the stresses in members a, b, and c for the structure shown in Fig. 134. $Ans.$ $a = 693$ lb. C; $b = 0$; $c = 400$ lb. T.

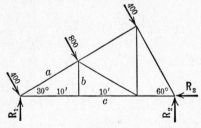

FIG. 134.

14. By the graphical method, solve for the reactions and stresses of the structure shown in Fig. 135.

$Ans.$ $R_2 = 430,000$ lb.; $LE = 270,000$ lb. C; $AK = 352,000$ lb. T.

15. The cable of a transmission line is suspended between towers 800 ft. apart. The cable weighs 1.5 lb. per ft., and the sag is 80 ft. Compute the maximum tension, using the catenary equations.   *Ans.* 1643 lb.

FIG. 135.

16. Solve for an approximate value of the maximum tension in the cable described in Prob. 15, using the parabolic method. What is the percentage of error?   *Ans.* 1616 lb.; 1.64 per cent.

CHAPTER IV

EQUILIBRIUM OF FORCES IN SPACE

Art. 26. Conditions of Equilibrium. The conditions of equilibrium for a system of non-coplanar forces are:

(1) The algebraic sum of the moments of the forces about any axis in space must equal zero.

(2) The algebraic sum of the components of the forces parallel to any given direction in space must equal zero.

(3) The polygon of the forces in space must close. It follows also that the projection of this polygon into any plane must close and hence the projection of the forces in space upon any plane in space must form a coplanar system of forces in equilibrium.

Art. 27. Concurrent Forces in Space. Any of the conditions of equilibrium stated above may be applied in the solution of a problem involving concurrent, non-coplanar forces. The following example illustrates the various possibilities.

Example

The frame shown in Fig. 136 (*a*) consists of three members *AD*, *CD*, and *DE* attached to a vertical wall *ACFG* and joined at *D* to support the 3000-lb. load. Determine the stress in each member of the frame.

Fig. 136.

Solution: First Method. The forces acting at *D*, as shown in Fig. 136 (*b*), constitute a system of concurrent, non-coplanar forces in equilibrium.

The additional dimensions shown in this figure can be determined from those originally given. Coordinate axes are taken as shown and the three force summations in the directions of these axes follow:

$$\Sigma F_x = AD \times \frac{4}{5} + CD \cos 45° - DE \times \frac{4}{7.2} = 0 \tag{1}$$

$$\Sigma F_y = DE \times \frac{6}{7.2} - 3000 = 0 \tag{2}$$

$$\Sigma F_z = AD \times \frac{3}{5} - CD \cos 45° = 0 \tag{3}$$

Simultaneous solution of these equations gives:

$$AD = 1430 \text{ lb. } T$$
$$CD = 1210 \text{ lb. } T$$
$$DE = 3600 \text{ lb. } C$$

Second Method. Instead of using force summations, three moment equations may be written, using as axes the lines AC, AF, and CG.

$$\Sigma M_{AC} = 3000 \times 4 - DE \times \frac{6}{7.2} \times 4 = 0 \qquad DE = 3600 \text{ lb. } C$$

$$\Sigma M_{AF} = CD \cos 45° \times 7 - 3600 \times \frac{4}{7.2} \times 3 = 0 \qquad CD = 1210 \text{ lb. } T$$

$$\Sigma M_{CG} = AD \times \frac{4}{5} \times 7 - 3600 \times \frac{4}{7.2} \times 4 = 0 \qquad AD = 1430 \text{ lb. } T$$

Third Method. If the forces of the Fig. 136 (b) are projected into the xy plane, a coplanar system results, consisting of the 3000-lb. load and force DE which appear in their real values since they lie in this plane,

Fig. 137.

and a third force Q which represents the combined projections of forces AD and CD. This projected system is shown in Fig. 137 (a).

This coplanar system can be solved in any of the usual ways. For instance:

$$\Sigma F_y = DE \times \frac{6}{7.2} - 3000 = 0 \qquad\qquad DE = 3600 \text{ lb. } C$$

$$\Sigma M_E = Q \times 6 - 3000 \times 4 = 0 \qquad\qquad Q = 2000 \text{ lb.}$$

The forces are now projected into the x–z plane as shown in Fig. 137 (b). Here the projection of DE will be the force Q reversed in direction. This coplanar system is then solved by any of the usual methods. For instance:

$$\Sigma M_A = 2000 \times 3 - CD \sin 45° \times 7 = 0 \qquad CD = 1210 \text{ lb. } T$$

$$\Sigma M_C = 2000 \times 4 - AD \times \tfrac{4}{5} \times 7 = 0 \qquad AD = 1430 \text{ lb. } T$$

The graphic method may also be applied to the above example, in which case the projections shown in Fig. 137 must be used.

Problems

1. Solve for the stress in each member of the frame shown in Fig. 138.

Ans. $AB = 1520$ lb. T; $AD = AF = 1250$ lb. C.

FIG. 138.

2. The frame shown in Fig. 139 is known as a shear-legs crane. Solve for the stress in each member of the crane.

Ans. $AB = 1570$ lb. T; $BC = BE = 860$ lb. C.

FIG. 139.

3. The legs of the tripod shown in Fig. 140 are 6 ft. long, and are spaced 120° apart. Solve for the stress in each leg.   *Ans.* 1540 lb. *C.*

4. Solve Prob. 3 if *B* is moved towards *C* so that the angle *BOC* is 90°.
    Ans. *AB* = 1690 lb. *C*; *AC* = 975 lb. *C*; *AD* = 1950 lb. *C.*

FIG. 140.   FIG. 141.

5. Solve for the stress in each member of the shear-legs crane in Fig. 141.
    Ans. *AB* = 3000 lb. *T*; *BC* = 2240 lb. *C*; *BE* = 1410 lb. *C.*

6. Solve Prob. 5 if the point where the line of the load strikes the ground is 15 ft. to the right of line *CE* and 10 ft. in front of line *AD.* (Suggestion: Resolve the 3000-lb. pull into three rectangular components at *B.*)
    Ans. *AB* = 1930 lb. *T*; *BC* = 1540 lb. *C*; *BE* = 2550 lb. *C.*

Art. 28. Parallel Forces in Space.

A table or platform carrying vertical loads and supported by vertical reactions constitutes a typical example of non-coplanar parallel forces. Three supports not in the same plane are sufficient for stability; any additional supports are redundant and make the system statically indeterminate. The solution may readily be made by means of the force summation and the summations of moments about convenient axes.

Example

The rectangular platform shown in Fig. 142 is supported at *A*, *B*, and *C* and carries a load of 600 lb. at the position indicated. Compute the reactions at the supports.

FIG. 142.

Solution: The necessary three equations may be chosen as follows:

$$\Sigma M_x = B \times 5 + C \times 1 - 600 \times 2 = 0 \tag{1}$$
$$\Sigma M_y = B \times 2 + C \times 8 - 600 \times 5 = 0 \tag{2}$$
$$\Sigma F = A + B + C - 600 = 0 \tag{3}$$

Simultaneous solution of these equations gives:

$$A = 94.4 \text{ lb.}; \quad B = 173.6 \text{ lb.}; \quad C = 332 \text{ lb.}$$

Problems

1. A rectangular platform is supported at A, B, and C, and carries a 1200-lb. load as shown in Fig. 143.   Solve for the reactions at the supports.

Ans. 400 lb. each.

FIG. 143.   FIG. 144.

2. A triangular platform with sides of 10 ft. each is supported at each vertex.   The platform weighs 200 lb. and carries an additional concentrated load of 400 lb. at a point situated on one of the medians and 3 ft. from the vertex.   Solve for the reactions at the supports.   (Note: The weight of the platform may be considered to act at the intersection of the medians.)

Ans. 328 lb.; 136 lb.; 136 lb.

3. A circular table top of 2-ft. radius has supports at A, B, and C, and carries a 400-lb. load located as shown in Fig. 144.   Determine the reaction at each support.   *Ans.* $A = 200$ lb.; $B = 157.5$ lb.; $C = 42.5$ lb.

4. Solve Prob. 3 if the support at B is moved 15° towards A.

Ans. $A = 174$ lb.; $B = 161$ lb.; $C = 65$ lb.

5. If a square platform is supported at one corner and at the midpoint of each of the opposite sides, show that each support carries one-third the weight of the platform.

Art. 29. Non-concurrent, Non-parallel Forces in Space.   This is the most general type of force system.   All the possible conditions of equilibrium may be needed to complete the solution of

such a system, but in general, projection into convenient planes will be found of most advantage.

Example 1

A vertical windlass weighing 150 lb. and supported in frictionless bearings at A and B is shown in Fig. 145 (a). The load W is raised by

FIG. 145.

means of the belt pulls applied to pulley C. The belt pulls are parallel to each other, and make an angle of 60° with the x–y plane as indicated. Determine the load W that can be raised, and the x, y, and z components of the bearing reactions.

Solution: The various forces acting on the windlass are first projected into the x–z plane and appear as shown in Fig. 145 (b).

$$\Sigma M_C = W \times \tfrac{1}{4} + 200 \times 1 - 400 \times 1 = 0$$

from which

$$W = 800 \text{ lb.}$$

The forces are now projected into the x–y plane as shown in Fig. 145 (c).

$$\Sigma M_A = B_x \times 6 + 300 \times 2 - 800 \times 4 = 0$$

$$B_x = 433 \text{ lb.}$$

$$\Sigma F_x = A_x + 433 + 300 - 800 = 0$$

$$A_x = 67 \text{ lb.}$$

Assuming that there is no way for the bearing at B to exert a vertical effect, the reaction $B_y = 0$. Then

$$\Sigma F_y = A_y - 150 = 0 \quad \text{and} \quad A_y = 150 \text{ lb.}$$

A third projection is then made into the y–z plane as shown in Fig. 145 (d), from which:

$$\Sigma M_A = 6B_z - 520 \times 2 = 0 \quad \text{gives} \quad B_z = 173 \text{ lb.}$$
$$\Sigma F_z = A_z + 173 - 520 = 0 \quad \text{gives} \quad A_z = 347 \text{ lb.}$$

Example 2

The crane shown in Fig. 146 (a) is supported by two backstays DG and DH. Determine the stress in each backstay when the plane of the boom BF bisects the angle GAH between the backstays.

Fig. 146.

Solution: The effect of the backstays in maintaining equilibrium of the crane may be represented by the forces D_V and D_H acting at D, as shown in Fig. 146 (b).

$$\Sigma M_A = D_H \times 12 - 3000 \times 16 = 0 \quad \text{gives} \quad D_H = 4000 \text{ lb.}$$

The horizontal plane at D now contains the horizontal components of DG and DH, of which D_H is the resultant. If the latter is reversed in direction, it becomes the equilibrant of the system as shown in Fig. 146 (c). It is evident by symmetry that DG_H and DH_H are equal. Their values may be obtained by:

$$\Sigma F_X = 2(DG_H \cos 60°) - 4000 = 0$$

from which
$$DG_H = DH_H = 4000 \text{ lb.}$$

Since each backstay is at 45° with the ground, the actual stress in each backstay may be found from the relation:

$$DG_H = DG \cos 45°$$

or
$$DG = DH = \frac{4000}{.707} = 5660 \text{ lb. } T$$

Example 3

Assuming that the boom of the crane in Ex. 2 above may be rotated in the horizontal plane about the mast, determine the position of the boom for maximum tension in DG. Solve for this stress and the corresponding stress in DH.

Solution: The position of the boom for maximum tension in DG is found in the following manner. Let the boom, and consequently D_H, be placed at any angle α with DH_H as shown in Fig. 147 (a). Let O be

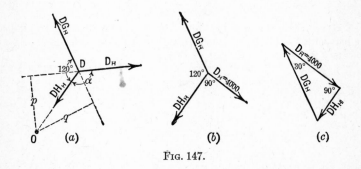

FIG. 147.

taken as any point on the line of action of DH_H and let p and q be the perpendicular distances from O to D_H and DG_H. Then:

$$\Sigma M_O = DG_H \times q - D_H \times p = 0$$

and

$$DG_H = D_H \times \frac{p}{q}$$

In this expression for DG_H, the factors D_H and q remain unchanged as the boom rotates. Therefore DG_H will be maximum when distance p is maximum. The maximum possible value of p, however, is the distance OD, and p has this value only when the angle α is 90° or 270°. Consequently, it follows that DG_H and hence DG itself will be maximum when the vertical plane of the boom is at right angles with the plane of the other backstay DH. When $\alpha = 90°$, the stress in DG will be maximum tension; when $\alpha = 270°$, the stress in DG will be maximum compression.

The solution for the stresses required is shown in Fig. 147 (b) and (c). D_H is placed at 90° with DH_H and the force triangle is drawn, from which

$$DG_H = \frac{4000}{\cos 30°} = 4620 \text{ lb.} \quad \text{and} \quad DH_H = 4000 \tan 30° = 2310 \text{ lb.}$$

The actual stresses in the backstays are then determined from their horizontal components.

$$\max DG = \frac{4620}{\cos 45°} = 6530 \text{ lb. } T;$$

$$DH = \frac{2310}{\cos 45°} = 3265 \text{ lb. } T$$

Any of the above examples may be solved graphically, using projections into convenient planes.

Problems

1. The windlass shown in Fig. 148 is driven by belt pulls T_2 and T_1 which are parallel to the z axis. Assuming that $T_2 = 2T_1$, determine the belt tensions and the components of the bearing reactions.

Ans. $T_2 = 150$ lb.; $A_y = 257$ lb.; $A_z = 32$ lb.; $B_y = 343$ lb.;
$B_z = 193$ lb.; $A_x = B_x = 0.$

FIG. 148.

2. The load on the windlass in Fig. 149 is held by force P acting perpendicular to the handle of the crank CD. The crank is $1\frac{1}{2}$ ft. long and stands

FIG. 149.

at 30° with the vertical. Solve for the force P and the y and z components of the bearing reactions at A and B.

Ans. $P = 55.5$ lb.; $A_y = 243$ lb.; $A_z = 12.0$ lb.; $B_y = 285$ lb.;
$B_z = 60.1$ lb.

3. The pole AB in Fig. 150 is braced by the backstays BC and BD. The 3000-lb. pull may be rotated about AB. Determine the value of angle α for maximum compression in AB. Solve for this stress and the corresponding stresses in BC and BD.

         Ans. $\alpha = 120°$; $AB = 6700$ lb. C; $BC = BD = 3670$ lb. T.

4. Determine the value of angle α in Fig. 150 for maximum tension in BC. Solve for this stress and the corresponding stresses in BD and AB.

         Ans. $\alpha = 90°$; $BC = 4240$ lb. T; $BD = 2120$ lb. T; $AB = 6000$ lb. C.

Fig. 150.   Fig. 151.

5. With the boom EG of the derrick shown in Fig. 151 in position for maximum tension in AB solve for the stresses in AB and AC.

         Ans. $AB = 2860$ lb. T; $AC = 1040$ lb. C.

Supplementary Problems

1. Three cords, each 8 ft. long, are hung from a horizontal ring 8 ft. in diameter and are joined at their lower ends to support a 100-lb. weight. On the ring, two of the cords are 90° apart and the third bisects the remaining arc. Determine the tension in each cord.

         Ans. 33.8 lb.; 33.8 lb.; 47.8 lb.

2. Solve Prob. 1 if the lengths of the first two cords are changed to 6 ft. each. *Ans.* 50.8 lb.; 50.8 lb.; 17.5 lb.

3. Solve for the stresses AD, CD, and DE in Fig. 152.

         Ans. $AD = 460$ lb. T; $CD = 460$ lb. T; $DE = 460$ lb. C.

Fig. 152.

4. Keeping the 600-lb. pull in the horizontal plane through D, Fig. 152, allow it to rotate 30° toward A and solve for the stresses.

         Ans. $AD = 50$ lb. C; $CD = 850$ lb. T; $DE = 400$ lb. C.

5. A 400-lb. sign is hung from a rod AB which is hinged to a vertical wall at A and braced by wires BC and BE as shown in Fig. 153. The sign is subjected to a wind pressure of 100 lb. normal to its surface on the side toward C. Assuming that the weight and wind pressure are divided equally between the hinge A and the joint B, solve for the compression in the rod and the tensions in the wires.   Ans. $AB = 267$ lb. C; $BC = 343$ lb. T; $BE = 284$ lb. T.

Fig. 153.   Fig. 154.

6. A horizontal circular platform of radius R is supported at three points A, B, and C on its circumference. A and B are 90° apart and C is 120° from A. The platform carries vertical loads of 500 lb. at its center and 100 lb. at a point D on the circumference diametrically opposite A. Determine the reactions at the supports.   Ans. $A = 48$ lb.; $B = 256$ lb.; $C = 296$ lb.

7. If the platform in Prob. 6 is not fastened to the support at A, what is the maximum load that can act at D before tipping occurs? Ans. 183 lb.

8. A vertical windlass, weighing 200 lb. and supported by frictionless bearings at A and B, is shown in Fig. 154. The load W is raised by means of the belt pulls applied to pulley C. The belt pulls lie in the horizontal plane of the pulley, are parallel to each other, and make an angle of 45° with the x axis as indicated. Determine the load W that can be raised, and the x, y, and z components of the bearing reactions.

Ans. $W = 1350$ lb.; $A_x = 516$ lb.; $B_x = 1150$ lb.; $A_y = 0$;
$B_y = 200$ lb.; $A_z = 159$ lb.; $B_z = 477$ lb.

9. A horizontal countershaft 6 ft. long and weighing 100 lb. is supported in bearings A and B at the ends. At 2 ft. from end A is a pulley of 2-ft. diameter weighing 80 lb. and carrying belt pulls of 600 lb. and 300 lb. acting vertically upward. At 2 ft. from end B is another pulley of $1\frac{1}{2}$-ft. diameter weighing 60 lb. and carrying horizontal belt pulls T_2 and T_1. Assuming that $T_2 = 2T_1$, determine the unknown belt pulls and the vertical and horizontal components of the bearing reactions.

Ans. $T_2 = 800$ lb.; $T_1 = 400$ lb.; $A_H = 400$ lb.; $A_V = 477$ lb;
$B_H = 800$ lb.; $B_V = 183$ lb.

10. Solve for the stresses in members AB and BC of the stiff-leg derrick shown in Fig. 155. If the boom AB is capable of rotation in the horizontal plane through A, state the value of α for (a) maximum tension in CD;

FIG. 155.

(b) maximum compression in CD; (c) maximum compression in AC. Solve for the stresses in AC, CD, and CE for each position.

    Ans.   (a) $\alpha = 90°$; $AC = 16{,}700$ lb. C; $CD = 16{,}600$ lb. T; $CE = 4280$ lb. C.

         (b) $\alpha = 270°$; $AC = 4690$ lb. T; $CD = 16{,}600$ lb. C; $CE = 4280$ lb. T.

         (c) $\alpha = 142.5°$; $AC = 23{,}500$ lb. C; $CD = 10{,}100$ lb. T; $CE = 10{,}100$ lb. T.

CHAPTER V

FRICTION

Art. 30. Fundamental Relations. Friction is the force exerted tangentially by one surface upon another with which it is in contact, tending to prevent motion of either surface relative to the other. As long as motion does not occur, the resistance to motion is known as *static friction*. When motion of one surface relative to the other does occur, the resistance is known as *kinetic friction*.

In Fig. 156 (*a*) the force P tends to cause motion of the block relative to the surface below, and the friction F tends to resist this

Fig. 156.

motion. As long as motion does not occur, the static friction F is just sufficient in amount to maintain static equilibrium. It is therefore an *adjustable* force, varying from zero to a maximum value which is reached when motion impends. This maximum value is known as the *limiting* static friction. The *coefficient* of static friction f is defined as the ratio of the limiting static friction F to the normal pressure N between the surfaces, or

$$f = \frac{F}{N}$$

The forces F and N in Fig. 156 (*a*) may be represented by their resultant R as shown in Fig. 156 (*b*). The angle ϕ between R and the normal to the surface is called the *angle of friction*. As the static friction increases, the angle ϕ increases and becomes a maximum when the condition of impending motion is reached. The maximum value of ϕ is called the limiting angle of friction. From Fig. 156

$$\text{max. } \phi = \tan^{-1}\frac{F}{N} = \tan^{-1}f$$

If the force P in Fig. 156 is increased to a value sufficient to overcome the maximum static friction, motion begins; the friction decreases and becomes *kinetic friction*. The ratio of the kinetic friction F to the normal pressure N is called the coefficient of kinetic friction and is also represented by f,

$$f = \frac{F}{N}$$

The coefficient of friction is determined by experiment, and the values thus obtained vary considerably as shown by the following table.

MATERIALS	STATIC f
Wood on wood	0.30 to 0.70
Metal on metal	0.15 to 0.30
Wood on metal	0.20 to 0.60
Leather on wood	0.25 to 0.50
Leather on metal	0.30 to 0.60

The coefficient of kinetic friction is somewhat less than that for static friction.

Art. 31. Angle of Repose and Cone of Friction. If the surface on which a body rests is gradually tilted, a position is eventually

(a)   *(b)*

Fig. 157.

reached such that the body is on the verge of slipping. In Fig. 157 (a) the angle θ represents the inclination of the surface when slipping impends and is called the *angle of repose.* From Fig. 157 (*b*)

$$\theta = \tan^{-1} \frac{F}{N}$$

It has previously been shown, however, that the limiting angle of static friction is

$$\phi = \tan^{-1} \frac{F}{N}$$

It thus follows that the angle of repose is equal to the limiting angle of static friction. Since the angle of repose represents the angle of inclination for impending slipping, a body placed on a surface inclined at any greater angle will slide down unless held, while a body placed on a surface inclined at a smaller angle will remain at rest unless acted upon by forces other than gravity.

The *cone of friction* is the cone generated by revolving, about the normal to the surface, a line inclined to the normal at an angle equal to the limiting angle of static friction, as shown in Fig. 158. If the resultant P of all external forces acting on the body, except the reaction R of the surface, lies within the cone of friction, no motion can occur since the equal and opposing surface reaction R must be acting at an angle with the normal less than the

Fig. 158.

limiting angle of static friction. Similarly, if P lies in the surface of the cone, motion is impending; and if P lies outside the cone, motion actually occurs.

Art. 32. Laws of Friction. The results of experiments by Coulomb, confirmed later by Morin, have led to the following laws of friction for dry surfaces:

1. Limiting static friction and kinetic friction are proportional to the normal pressure. In other words, the coefficient of friction is independent of the normal pressure.

2. The coefficient of friction is independent of the area of contact.

3. The coefficient of kinetic friction is less than that for static friction and for low speeds is independent of the relative velocity of the surfaces.

4. Friction is only slightly affected by ordinary temperature changes.

The laws of friction for lubricated surfaces differ greatly from those for dry surfaces. For instance, the friction is practically independent of the nature of the surfaces and of the normal pressure as long as a film of lubricant lies between the surfaces. The temperature greatly affects the friction of lubricated surfaces.

Art. 33. Equilibrium Involving Friction. The conditions of static equilibrium as previously stated also apply, of course, to a system of forces in which friction is involved. The reaction of the surface upon the free body with which it is in contact may be represented by its normal and tangential components, N and F, or by the resultant reaction R inclined at angle ϕ to the normal. If slipping impends or actually occurs, $F = fN$ and $\phi = \tan^{-1} f$. If slipping is neither occurring nor impending, the friction force F and the angle ϕ are merely sufficient to maintain equilibrium. The direction of the frictional reaction is always such as to *oppose the motion* of the free body; or it may be stated as being in the direction that the rubbing surface tends to move *relative* to the free body.

Problems of equilibrium involving friction may be solved by graphic, trigonometric, or algebraic methods. In the graphic or trigonometric solutions, the resultant reaction R at the rubbing surface must be used. The proper position of R is easily laid out graphically. For instance, if the coefficient of friction is 0.3, ten units to any convenient scale are laid out in a direction perpendicular to the surface; then three units to the same scale are laid out in a direction parallel to the surface. Thus the tangent of the angle of the resulting diagonal with the normal is 0.3 and conforms to the requirements.

Example 1

Determine the force P in Fig. 159 (*a*) to produce impending motion of the block up the plane if the coefficient of friction is 0.3.

Solution: First Method. The free-body diagram of the block is shown in Fig. 159 (*b*) with the reaction at the surface represented by its components F and N. Since slipping impends, $F = fN = 0.3N$. The friction F is directed down the plane because it must oppose the motion of the free body; this is also the direction of impending motion of the plane relative to the free body.   Force summations are now made in the x and y directions as indicated.

$$\Sigma F_y = N - 200 \cos 30° - P \sin 45° = 0$$

$$\Sigma F_x = P \cos 45° - 200 \sin 30° - 0.3N = 0$$

Simultaneous solution of these equations gives $P = 307$ lb.

Fig. 159.

Second Method. The free-body diagram of the block is shown again in Fig. 160 (a) but with the components F and N of the surface reaction replaced by their resultant R which acts at an angle ϕ with the normal to the surface.

$$\phi = \tan^{-1} f = \tan^{-1} 0.3 = 16.7°$$

Fig. 160.

Since the number of forces acting on the free body is now reduced to three, a solution may be made trigonometrically from the force triangle shown in Fig. 160 (b).

$$\frac{P}{\sin 46.7°} = \frac{200}{\sin 28.3°} \qquad\qquad P = 307 \text{ lb.}$$

The same result is obtained by summation of forces in the x direction, Fig. 160 (a), at 90° with R.

$$\Sigma F_x = P \cos 61.7° - 200 \cos 43.3° = 0 \quad P = 307 \text{ lb.}$$

The solution may also be made graphically.

Example 2

The coefficient of friction is 0.2 between the ladder and wall, Fig. 161 (a), and 0.5 between ladder and floor. Determine the force P,

Fig. 161.

applied horizontally at the bottom, to produce impending motion to the left.

Solution: The free-body diagram of the ladder is shown in Fig. 161 (b), the reaction at each rubbing surface being represented by its F and N components. The conditions of equilibrium are applied as follows:

$$\Sigma M_A = N_B \times 20 + 0.2 N_B \times 15 - 60 \times 7.5 = 0 \quad N_B = 19.6 \text{ lb.}$$
$$\Sigma F_V = N_A - 60 + 0.2(19.6) = 0 \qquad\qquad N_A = 56.1 \text{ lb.}$$
$$\Sigma F_H = P - 0.5(56.1) + 19.6 = 0 \qquad\qquad P = 8.45 \text{ lb.}$$

Problems

1. Solve for the horizontal force P required to produce impending motion of a 40-lb. block up a 15° plane if $f = 0.3$.

Ans. $P = 24.7$ lb.

2. Solve Prob. 1 for impending motion down the plane.

Ans. $P = -1.19$ lb.

8. Solve for the least force P and its angle with the plane to start the block of Prob. 1 up the plane. *Ans.* 21.0 lb.; 16.7°.

4. If $f = 0.25$ for both blocks in Fig. 162, determine the value of W for impending motion. *Ans.* $W = 114$ lb.

5. If the weight W in Fig. 162 is 300 lb. determine the tension in the cord and the friction under W. *Ans.* $T = 28.3$ lb.; $F = 28.3$ lb.

6. A uniform ladder 20 ft. long weighing 100 lb. is placed with its upper end against a vertical wall and its lower end on a horizontal floor. If the ladder is placed at 30° with the vertical and $f = 0.3$ for both wall and floor, what vertical load can be placed at the upper end of the ladder before it starts to slip?   *Ans.* 13.4 lb.

Fɪɢ. 162.   Fɪɢ. 163.

7. The hanger ABC shown in Fig. 163 slides up and down the vertical post. If $f = 0.3$, determine the minimum distance x at which a load W may be placed without causing the hanger to slide down. Neglect the weight of the hanger. (Solve algebraically and graphically.)

Ans. $x = 13.5$ in.

Art. 34. Wedge and Block.

Wedges are used as lifting devices, keys for shafting, etc. In the solution of problems involving the wedge, it is usually more convenient to make use of the resultant reaction at the rubbing surfaces. Graphic, trigonometric, or algebraic procedures may be used.

Example

The coefficient of friction is 0.25 at all rubbing surfaces for the wedge and block shown in Fig. 164. Determine the force P to start the wedge downward.

Solution: The block B is selected as the first free body as shown in Fig. 165 (*a*). The friction angle is 14°, since $\phi = \tan^{-1} f = \tan^{-1} .25$. Since slipping is impending, the resulting reactions R_1 and R_2 act at this angle with the normal to each of the sliding surfaces and are inclined in the directions in which the sliding surfaces tend to move relative to the free body.

Fɪɢ. 164.

The system of forces may now be solved graphically by drawing to scale the force triangle shown in Fig. 165 (b), from which R_2 scales 397 lb.

The solution may be made trigonometrically by applying the law of sines to the force triangle,

$$\frac{R_2}{\sin 14°} = \frac{1200}{\sin 47°} \qquad R_2 = 397 \text{ lb.}$$

Fig. 165.

The solution may be made algebraically from Fig. 165 (a) by placing the x axis at 90° with R_1 and applying $\Sigma F_x = 0$,

$$\Sigma F_x = R_2 \cos 43° - 1200 \sin 14° = 0 \qquad R_2 = 397 \text{ lb.}$$

Fig. 166.

The wedge A is now taken as a free body as shown in Fig. 166 (a). The proper positions for the reactions are determined in the same manner as for the preceding free body. The force triangle is shown in Fig. 166 (b), and the trigonometric solution gives

$$\frac{P}{\sin 43°} = \frac{397}{\sin 76°} \qquad P = 279 \text{ lb.}$$

Problems

1. The angle of friction for the wedge and block in Fig. 167 is 15°. Solve for the force P required for impending motion of the wedge toward the right. (The block rubs on one side only.)   *Ans.* $P = 4290$ lb.

2. In Fig. 167, solve for force P required for impending motion of the wedge to the left.   *Ans.* $P = -635$ lb.

FIG. 167.   FIG. 168.

3. Solve Prob. 2 if the angle of friction is 30°.   *Ans.* $P = -2460$ lb.

4. If $f = 0.2$ for all surfaces, what resistance Q in Fig. 168 can be overcome by the 200-lb. force applied to the wedge?   *Ans.* $Q = 325$ lb.

Art. 35. The Jackscrew.

The jackscrew is a mechanical device used to raise or lower heavy loads. The threads of the screw may be either square or triangular, but only the square thread will be considered here. The thread may be considered as an inclined plane wound around a cylinder. The operation of raising or lowering a load consists essentially of pushing the load up or down an inclined plane by means of a horizontal force applied to the end of a lever. In Fig. 169 (a), P is the horizontal force acting at the end of the lever of length l; p is the pitch of the thread; θ is the pitch angle; and r is the mean radius of the thread. The effect of force P acting on the lever is to produce an equivalent horizontal pressure Q which acts at the mean radius from the axis of the screw and which is given by

$$Q = \frac{Pl}{r}$$

The pitch angle θ is given by,

$$\theta = \tan^{-1} \frac{p}{2\pi r}$$

Although the load is actually distributed over the circumference of several threads, for convenience it will be considered as acting over a small section as shown in Fig. 169 (b). Here, one

Fig. 169.

turn of the thread has been unwound and is shown as an inclined plane. In this case the load W is being pushed up the plane by the horizontal force Q. The reaction R at the rubbing surface acts at the angle of friction ϕ with the normal to the surface, where $\phi = \tan^{-1} f$. From the triangle of forces, shown in Fig. 169 (c),

$$Q = W \tan (\phi + \theta)$$

and

$$P = \frac{Qr}{l} = \frac{Wr}{l} \tan (\phi + \theta) \text{ to raise the load}$$

When the load is being lowered, the resultant R lies on the other side of the normal to the surface and, by following the same procedure as above, P is given by

$$P = \frac{Qr}{l} = \frac{Wr}{l} \tan (\phi - \theta) \text{ to lower the load}$$

It is evident from the latter equation that, when $\phi = \theta$, the load will be on the verge of slipping down without application of any force.   If, then, θ is greater than ϕ, the load will not remain at rest unless held by a resisting force P.   For the jackscrew to be self-locking, that is for the load to be held by friction alone, ϕ must be greater than θ.   Since $\phi = \tan^{-1} f$ and $\theta = \tan^{-1} \dfrac{p}{2\pi r}$, it follows that the pitch p must be less than $2\pi r f$.

Problems

1. The mean radius of the threads of a jackscrew is 2 in. and the pitch is $\frac{3}{8}$ in.   If $f = 0.07$, determine the force P applied at the end of a lever 20 in. long to raise a load of 5000 lb.   *Ans.* $P = 50$ lb.

2. Determine the force P in Prob. 1 to lower the weight.
                                                                        Ans. $P = 20$ lb.

3. A hand-press has four square-threaded screws to the inch with a mean diameter of $1\frac{1}{2}$ in.   If $f = 0.1$, what pressure W can be exerted by the press if a force of 50 lb. is applied at the end of a 24-in. lever?   Is the screw self-locking?   *Ans.* $W = 10,400$ lb.; yes.

Art. 36. Axle Friction and the Friction Circle.

Owing to a slight but necessary difference between the diameters of an axle or journal and the bearing in which it rotates, contact takes place between the two along a small arc instead of around the complete circumference.   In the case of a frictionless bearing, the resultant reaction between journal and bearing would pass through their center and through the point of contact.   If there is friction, however, the journal will roll along the surface of the bearing until the resultant reaction acts at the angle of friction ϕ with the normal line or radius at the point of contact, when slipping of the journal on the bearing will occur.

Fig. 170.

As the journal continues to rotate, it will remain in this position, which is shown in Fig. 170.   Here the journal is rotating clockwise in a stationary bearing and rolls up the side of the bearing until slipping begins.   The resultant reaction R does not pass through the center but is tangent to a small circle, concentric with the journal, whose radius is $r_1 = r \sin \phi$. This circle is called the *friction circle*. If the coefficient of friction is small, $\sin \phi$ may be replaced by $\tan \phi$. Thus $r_1 = r \tan \phi = fr$.

When the radius r of the bearing and the coefficient f are known, the friction circle is determined and may be used to locate the position of the bearing reaction. The reaction is always tangent to the friction circle on the side toward which the journal rolls. The use of the friction circle is of particular advantage in the graphic determination of reactions and stresses in mechanisms.

Example

A freight car weighing 250,000 lb. has wheels of 33-in. diameter and axles of 6-in. diameter. If the coefficient of axle friction is 0.02, determine the drawbar pull on the car necessary to overcome axle friction.

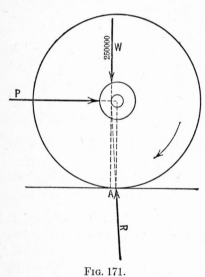

Fig. 171.

Solution: For purposes of solution, the entire weight may be considered as acting on one wheel which is shown as a free body in Fig. 171. The wheel is acted upon by three forces, the weight $W = 250,000$ lb. acting vertically downward, P representing the horizontal pressure of the car against the axle, and the reaction R of the track on the wheel. The reaction R must pass through the point of contact between wheel and track and also be tangent to the friction circle. Contact between axle and bearing occurs along the top. As the axle turns clockwise, it tends to roll to the left on the bearing; hence R is tangent on the left side. Forces P and W must intersect somewhere on the line of action of R. In the figure, P is shown as acting through the center; W will then be approximately tangent to the friction circle and may be taken as actually tangent without appreciable error.

The radius of the friction circle is $r' = fr = 0.02 \times 3 = 0.06$ in.

The equation $\Sigma M_A = 0$ then gives $P \times 16.5 - 250,000 \times 0.06 = 0$, from which $P = 910$ lb.

From the figure, it is seen that P is equal to the component of R

representing the resistance offered by the track to the forward motion of the car. Since the drawbar pull acting on the car must be just sufficient to overcome the resistance at the track, it follows that P is the value of the required drawbar pull.

Problems

1. A 100,000-lb. car has 33-in.-diameter wheels and 6-in.-diameter axles. If $f = 0.06$ at the bearings, determine the drawbar pull P required to move the car up a 1 per cent grade.   *Ans. $P = 2090$ lb.*

2. Determine the steepest grade on which the car of Prob. 1 would not start down.   *Ans.* 1.09 per cent.

3. Fig. 172 represents a pulley of 2-ft. diameter mounted on a 3-in.-

Fig. 172.

diameter axle. The coefficient of axle friction is 0.08. Solve for the force P required to raise the 600-lb. load with uniform speed.   *Ans. $P = 612$ lb.*

4. Solve for the force P required to lower the load in Prob. 3 with uniform speed.   *Ans. $P = 588$ lb.*

Art. 37. Rolling Resistance.

If a wheel or roller and the track or roadway on which it rests were absolutely rigid, no resistance would be encountered at the track to the rolling of the wheel. Owing to the elasticity of the materials, however, deformations will occur, the track being somewhat depressed, and the surface of the wheel slightly flattened out. A resistance is thus set up to the rolling of the wheel, the effect being equivalent to a small obstruction constantly in front of the wheel. This resistance is called *rolling resistance*, or less accurately, rolling friction.

In Fig. 173 is shown a wheel carrying a vertical load W and pulled forward by a horizontal force P applied at the axle. The resultant reaction R of the track acts through a point B at distance

a in front of the vertical radius. If motion is uniform and the depression of the surface is small, $\Sigma M_B = 0$ gives

$$P \cdot r = W \cdot a \quad \text{(approximately)}$$

$$P = \frac{Wa}{r}$$

FIG. 173.   FIG. 174.

If the load rests on the surface of the roller and the force P is applied to the load as is shown in Fig. 174, a similar relation may be obtained.

$$\Sigma M_B = 2Pr - W(a + a_1) = 0 \quad \text{(approximately)}$$

$$P = \frac{W(a + a_1)}{2r}$$

The arrangement in Fig. 174 is commonly used for moving very heavy objects.

Although the results of many investigations of rolling resistance are not in entire agreement, it appears that the distance a is practically constant for a given material, being independent, within reasonable limits, of the load and the radius of the wheel. It is called the *coefficient* of rolling resistance. The values of the coefficient, obtained from experiments of several investigators, are given for a few materials in the table below.

MATERIALS	a (inches)
Elm on oak.....................	0.0327
Steel on steel...................	0.007 to 0.020
Steel on wood..................	0.06 to 0.10
Steel on soft earth..............	3.0 to 5.0

The fact that the coefficient of rolling resistance is very low for hardened steel is put to practical use in ball and roller bearings.

Example

Determine the pull required to keep in uniform motion on a level track a 100,000-lb. car having 33-in.-diameter wheels and 6-in.-diameter axles, if the coefficient of axle friction is 0.05, and the coefficient of rolling resistance is 0.01 in.

Solution: The load may be taken as acting on a single wheel as shown in Fig. 175. The radius of the friction circle is $fr = 3 \times 0.05 = 0.15$ in. The reaction R of the track must pass through the point A at 0.01 in. in front of the vertical radius and must also be tangent to the friction circle. With load P acting through the center of the wheel and axle, the load W, passing through the intersection of P and R, will be very nearly tangent to the friction circle

Fig. 175.

and its distance from A will thus be 0.01 in. + 0.15 in. = 0.16 in.   The equation $\Sigma M_A = 0$ then gives

$$P \times 16.5 = 100,000 \times .16$$

$$P = 970 \text{ lb.}$$

Problems

1. Solve for the pull required to move the car in the above example up a 1 per cent grade with uniform speed.   *Ans. P = 1970 lb.*

2. If the pull required to overcome the rolling resistance of a freight car is 2 lb. per ton of weight, what is the value of the coefficient?   Use 33-in.-diameter wheels.   *Ans. a = 0.0165 in.*

3. A 2-ton weight is to be moved by use of 2-in.-diameter rollers.   If the coefficient of rolling resistance for the rollers and floor is 0.007, and that for rollers and weight is 0.02, determine the pull required.   *Ans. 54 lb.*

Art. 38. Belt or Band Friction.

The transmission of power by belt or rope drive is dependent on friction between the pulley surface and the belt or rope.   The holding of large loads by means of band brakes, ropes wound around posts, etc., is similarly dependent on friction.   Fig. 176 (a) shows a pulley of any radius r driven by a belt whose angle of contact with the pulley surface is β.   The tension T_2 on the driving side of the belt is greater than the tension T_1 on the slack side.   A portion of the belt of differential length ds with an angle of contact $d\theta$ is shown as a free body in Fig. 176 (b).   The normal pressure on this piece of the belt is represented by dN and the friction by dF.   If T is the belt tension on the slack side, then the tension on the driving side is $T + dT$.

FIG. 176.

The free body is in equilibrium under the action of the four forces and ΣM_0 gives

$$(T + dT)\cdot r - T\cdot r - dF\cdot r = 0$$

from which

$$dT = dF \tag{1}$$

The equation $\Sigma F_y = 0$ gives

$$dN - T \sin \frac{d\theta}{2} - (T + dT) \sin \frac{d\theta}{2} = 0$$

$$dN = 2T \sin \frac{d\theta}{2} + dT \sin \frac{d\theta}{2}$$

The term $dT \sin \dfrac{d\theta}{2}$ is negligible since it is an infinitesimal of higher order.   Since $\dfrac{d\theta}{2}$ is an infinitesimal angle, $\sin \dfrac{d\theta}{2}$ may be replaced by $\dfrac{d\theta}{2}$.   The preceding equation then becomes

$$dN = Td\theta \tag{2}$$

When slipping of belt on pulley surface impends or occurs,

$$dF = fdN \qquad (3)$$

Equations (1), (2), and (3) may now be combined,

$$dT = dF = fdN = fTd\theta$$

or

$$\frac{dT}{T} = fd\theta$$

The above equation may be integrated to obtain the relation between T_2 and T_1 as follows:

$$\int_{T_1}^{T_2} \frac{dT}{T} = f \int_0^\beta d\theta$$

$$\log_e \frac{T_2}{T_1} = f\beta \qquad (4)$$

or

$$\frac{T_2}{T_1} = e^{f\beta} \qquad (5)$$

or

$$\log_{10} \frac{T_2}{T_1} = f\beta \log_{10}e = 0.4343\,f\beta \qquad (6)$$

In the above equations, the angle β is in radians and T_2 must be the larger of the two tensions. The same relations apply to a band brake or to a rope wrapped around a post. It should be particularly noted that the equations hold only for the condition of *slipping impending or actually occurring.*

Problems

1. A weight of 800 lb. is to be lowered uniformly by means of a cable making 2.4 turns around a snubbing post. If $f = 0.3$, what force is required at the slack end of the cable?   *Ans.* 8.7 lb.

2. How many turns of rope around a snubbing post are required for a force of 50 lb. on the slack end to hold a load of 25,000 lb. at the other end if $f = 0.4$?   *Ans.* 2.48 turns.

3. A belt runs between two pulleys of equal diameter for which $f = 0.5$. If the tension in the slack side of the belt is 300 lb., what tension can be developed in the taut side before the belt will start to slip? *Ans.* 1440 lb.

4. A band brake as shown in Fig. 177 is used to control the motion of the load. If $f = 0.4$ for the band, what force P must be applied to the lever in order that the load may descend with uniform speed? *Ans. P* = 14.3 lb.

FIG. 177.

Supplementary Problems

1. In Fig. 178, the blocks A and B are connected by a stiff rod. If the coefficient of friction is 0.25 for both bodies, will the system move? Determine the friction under each body and the compression in the rod.

           Ans. No motion; $F_A = 21.0$ lb.; $F_B = 44.6$ lb.; 51.4 lb. *C*.

2. What horizontal force applied to B is required to start the system in Prob. 1 toward the right?   *Ans. P* = 11.8 lb.

3. What are the amount and direction of the *least* pull P that will start the system of Prob. 1 toward the right?   *Ans. P* = 11.4 lb.; $\theta_H = 14°$.

FIG. 178.

FIG. 179.

4. A uniform ladder is placed against a vertical wall with its lower end on a horizontal floor. If $f = 0.4$ for both wall and floor, at what maximum angle with the wall may the ladder be inclined before slipping impends?

                                          Ans. 43.6°.

5. If the ladder of Prob. 4 is 15 ft. long, weighs 60 lb., and is inclined at 30° with the wall, how far up the ladder may a weight of 125 lb. be placed before slipping impends?   *Ans.* 12.7 ft.

6. If the coefficient of friction is 0.15 for all surfaces of the wedge and block in Fig. 179, what weight W can be raised?   *Ans.* 500 lb.

7. Determine the maximum angle that the wedge and inclined plane of

Prob. 6 could have and still, by means of friction only, be able to keep the load W from descending.   *Ans.* 17°.

8. The double pulley shown in Fig. 180 weighs 400 lb. and is mounted on an axle of 2-in. diameter. If the coefficient of axle friction is 0.15, what force P is required to raise the load?   *Ans.* 418 lb.

FIG. 180.   FIG. 181.

9. If the spool shown in Fig. 181 weighs 800 lb. and the coefficient of rolling resistance is 0.15 in., determine the force P required to maintain uniform motion.   *Ans.* 4 lb.

10. If a pull of 20 lb. at the slack end of a rope passing $2\frac{1}{2}$ times around a spar holds a load of 8000 lb., what is the coefficient of friction?

Ans. 0.381.

11. If $f = 0.3$ for both band brake and the incline in Fig. 182, determine the weight W that can be kept from slipping by the 60-lb. force applied to the brake lever.   *Ans.* 2280 lb.

FIG. 182.   FIG. 183.

12. Determine the frictional moment produced on the rotating drum in Fig. 183 by the band brake if the coefficient of friction for the brake is 0.4.

Ans. 1470 in-lb.

13. The load shown in Fig. 184 is in impending motion down the plane. If f for all surfaces is 0.25 and the cable is wrapped $2\frac{1}{3}$ times around the post A, compute the required tension T. *Ans.* 192 lb.

FIG. 184. FIG. 185.

14. Compute force P to cause impending motion to the right for the block shown in Fig. 185. Use $f = 0.268$. *Ans.* 74.1 lb.

15. Solve Prob. 14 for the least force P to produce impending motion. *Ans.* 71.6 lb.

CHAPTER VI

CENTROIDS AND CENTER OF GRAVITY

Art. 39. Center of Gravity of a Material Body. The resultant of the attractions of gravity exerted upon all the particles composing a material body is known as the weight of the body. In the case of a rigid body it can be shown that, regardless of the position into which the body is turned, this resultant force always acts through a certain point fixed in the body. This fixed point, at which the entire weight of the body may be considered to be concentrated, is called the *center of gravity* of the body.

To locate the resultant of a system of parallel forces, the principle of moments is used as shown in Art. 6. Let W denote the weight of the body, and w_1, w_2, w_3, etc., the weights of individual particles or parts; let x_1, x_2, x_3, etc., be the distances of these particles or parts from the y–z plane; and let $\bar{x}$ (called *bar x* or *gravity x*) be the distance of the center of gravity of the entire body from the y–z plane. The following moment equation may then be written:

$$W\bar{x} = w_1x_1 + w_2x_2 + w_3x_3 + \text{etc.}$$

until all parts have been included. Similarly, by moments with respect to the xz plane,

$$W\bar{y} = w_1y_1 + w_2y_2 + w_3y_3 + \text{etc.}$$

and, by moments with respect to the x–y plane:

$$W\bar{z} = w_1z_1 + w_2z_2 + w_3z_3 + \text{etc.}$$

Art. 40. Centroids of Volumes, Areas, and Lines. If the material composing a homogeneous, rigid body is removed from the volume or space which it occupies, the point within that volume formerly known as the center of gravity of the body is now called the *centroid* of the volume.   By the principle of moments applied to the volume and its parts, the following equations result:

$$V\bar{x} = v_1x_1 + v_2x_2 + v_3x_3 + \text{etc.}$$

$$V\bar{y} = v_1y_1 + v_2y_2 + v_3y_3 + \text{etc.}$$

$$V\bar{z} = v_1z_1 + v_2z_2 + v_3z_3 + \text{etc.}$$

It should be noted that this set of equations may be obtained from those of Art. 39 by dividing each term by a density factor.

If the body consists of a homogeneous thin shell, the limiting position of the center of gravity of the shell as the thickness approaches zero becomes the *centroid* of the resulting surface area. The moment equations necessary to locate the centroid of an area are:

$$A\bar{x} = A_1x_1 + A_2x_2 + A_3x_3 + \text{etc.}$$

$$A\bar{y} = A_1y_1 + A_2y_2 + A_3y_3 + \text{etc.}$$

$$A\bar{z} = A_1z_1 + A_2z_2 + A_3z_3 + \text{etc.}$$

In similar manner, if a body consists of a homogeneous slender rod, the limiting position of the center of gravity of the rod, as the cross section approaches zero becomes the *centroid* of the resulting line.   The following equations locate the position:

$$l\bar{x} = l_1x_1 + l_2x_2 + l_3x_3 + \text{etc.}$$

$$l\bar{y} = l_1y_1 + l_2y_2 + l_3y_3 + \text{etc.}$$

$$l\bar{z} = l_1z_1 + l_2z_2 + l_3z_3 + \text{etc.}$$

The terms center of gravity and centroid are often used interchangeably.

Art. 41. Center of Gravity and Centroids by Symmetry.   The centroid of any figure which possesses a line of symmetry must obviously lie on that line.   If there are two or more such lines of symmetry, the centroid will lie at their intersection.   If there exists a plane of symmetry, the centroid must be in this plane. When there are two planes of symmetry, the centroid must lie on their line of intersection.   The same statements apply to the location of the center of gravity of any material body which is homogeneous throughout.

In this way may be determined partly or completely the location of the centroids of many objects.   To illustrate, the following cases are given:

The centroid of any straight line is at its midpoint.

The centroid of a circular arc is on the bisecting radius.

The centroid of the area of a rectangle is at its geometric center.

The centroid of a sector of a circle is on the bisecting radius.

The centroid of a right circular cone or cylinder is on its geometric axis.

Art. 42. Centroids by Integration.   In cases where an object cannot be divided into a few simple parts for the purpose of obtaining the necessary moment equations for locating the centroid, the same principle may still be used by dividing the object into an infinite number of differential parts.   The right-hand member of a given moment equation then becomes a summation of an infinite number of differential terms, resulting in an integral.   Thus, for an area, the equations would be:

$$A\bar{x} = x_1 dA_1 + x_2 dA_2 + x_3 dA_3 + \text{etc} = \int x\, dA$$

Similarly, for lines and volumes,

$$l\bar{x} = \int x\, dl$$

$$V\bar{x} = \int x\, dV$$

By assigning proper limits to the integral and evaluating, the coordinates of the centroid may be determined.

Example 1

Determine the location of the centroid of a circular arc.

Solution: Let r be the radius of the arc and α the angle subtended at its center. Let coordinate axes be taken with the origin at the center and the x-axis bisecting the arc, as shown in Fig. 186.   Then $\bar{y} = 0$ by symmetry.   By moments with respect to the y axis,

$$l\bar{x} = \int x\, dl$$

FIG. 186.

In the figure, $l = r\alpha$, $dl = r\,d\theta$, and $x = r\cos\theta$. Thus

$$r\alpha\bar{x} = \int_{-\frac{\alpha}{2}}^{+\frac{\alpha}{2}} r\cos\theta \cdot r\,d\theta$$

and

$$\bar{x} = \frac{2r}{\alpha}\sin\frac{\alpha}{2}$$

For a semi-circular arc, $\alpha = \pi$, and $\bar{x} = 2r/\pi$. The same expression, $\bar{x} = 2r/\pi$, also applies to an arc of 90°, giving the distance of the centroid from the bounding radii.

Example 2

FIG. 187.

Show that the centroid of the area of a triangle is located at a distance of one-third the altitude from the base.

Solution: Let b and h represent the base and altitude, respectively, of any triangle. Place the triangle with its base on the x axis as shown in Fig. 187. By moments with respect to the x axis:

$$A\bar{y} = \int y\,dA$$

where

$$A = \frac{bh}{2} \quad \text{and} \quad dA = u\,dy$$

thus

$$\frac{bh}{2}\,\bar{y} = \int y \cdot u\,dy$$

Since, by similar triangles, $\dfrac{u}{b} = \dfrac{h-y}{h}$,

$$\frac{bh}{2}\,\bar{y} = \int_{0}^{h} y \cdot \frac{b}{h}\,(h-y)\,dy$$

$$\bar{y} = \frac{h}{3}$$

Example 3

Locate the centroid of the area of a sector of a circle.

Solution: Let the sector of radius r and angle α be placed with its

center at the origin and with the x axis bisecting the angle, as shown in Fig. 188.   Then $\bar{y} = 0$, by symmetry.
The differential area shown is actually a differential sector which may be treated as a triangle.

$$A\bar{x} = \int x \, dA$$

where

$$dA = \tfrac{1}{2} r^2 \, d\theta$$

$$A = \int dA = \int_{-\frac{\alpha}{2}}^{+\frac{\alpha}{2}} \tfrac{1}{2} \, r^2 \, d\theta = \frac{r^2\alpha}{2}$$

Fig. 188

$$x = \tfrac{2}{3} r \cos \theta$$

thus

$$\frac{r^2\alpha}{2} \, \bar{x} = \int_{-\frac{\alpha}{2}}^{+\frac{\alpha}{2}} \tfrac{2}{3} \, r \cos \theta \cdot \tfrac{1}{2} \, r^2 \, d\theta$$

and

$$\bar{x} = \frac{4r}{3\alpha} \sin \frac{\alpha}{2}$$

For a semicircle, $\alpha = \pi$ and $\bar{x} = 4r/3\pi$.   The same expression also gives the centroidal distance for a quadrant with respect to the bounding radii.

Example 4

Show that the centroid of the volume of a cone or pyramid is at three-fourths the altitude from the vertex.

Solution: The altitude of the cone is represented by h, and the base, which may be any shape, has area A. The vertex of the cone is placed at the origin with the base parallel to the x axis as shown in Fig. 189.   The differential volume is a thin slice parallel to the base.   Let A' represent the area of the slice.   From the geometry of the figure, $A'/A = y^2/h^2$.   By moments with respect to the x axis:

Fig. 189.

$$V\bar{y} = \int y \, dV$$

where

$$V = \tfrac{1}{3} Ah, \quad \text{and} \quad dV = A'dy = \frac{A}{h^2} y^2 dy$$

thus

$$\tfrac{1}{3}Ah\,\bar{y} = \int_0^h y \cdot \frac{A}{h^2}\, y^2 dy$$

and

$$\bar{y} = \tfrac{3}{4}h$$

Example 5

Locate the centroid of the volume of the solid of revolution obtained by rotating about the x axis the area bounded by the parabola $y^2 = 2x$, the x axis, and the line $x = 8$.

Solution: The solid of revolution described is shown in Fig. 190. By symmetry, $\bar{y} = 0$ and $\bar{z} = 0$. The differential volume is taken as a thin disk as shown.

Fig. 190.

$$dV = \pi y^2\, dx = 2\pi x\, dx$$
$$V = \int dV = \int_0^8 2\pi x\, dx = 64\pi$$

By moments with respect to the yz plane

$$V\bar{x} = \int x\, dV \quad \text{or} \quad 64\pi\bar{x} = \int_0^8 x \cdot 2\pi x\, dx$$

whence

$$\bar{x} = 5.33$$

Problems

1. Solve Ex. 3 above by using $dA = \rho\alpha d\rho$ as shown in Fig. 191.

2. Solve Ex. 3 above by using $dA = \rho d\rho d\theta$ as shown in Fig. 192.

Fig. 191.

Fig. 192.

3. Determine by integration the distance of the centroid of the curved surface of a right circular cone from the vertex.   *Ans.* $\tfrac{2}{3}h$.

4. Determine by integration the distance of the centroid of the curved surface of a hemisphere from the bounding plane.   *Ans.* $\frac{1}{2}r$.

5. By integration locate the centroid of the volume of a hemisphere with respect to the bounding plane.

$$Ans. \ \frac{3}{8}r.$$

6. Locate the centroid of the shaded area shown in Fig. 193.

$$Ans. \ \bar{x} = \tfrac{3}{10}a; \ \bar{y} = \tfrac{3}{4}b.$$

7. Locate the centroid of the area bounded by the parabola of Fig. 193, the x axis, and the line $x = a$.

$$Ans. \ \bar{x} = \tfrac{3}{5}a; \ \bar{y} = \tfrac{3}{8}b.$$

Fig. 193.

Art. 43. Centroids of Composite Bodies.

A composite body is one which can be divided into two or more simple parts, each of which has a centroid whose position is already known. Such a body may be a solid having weight, or a volume, surface, or line. The centroid of the body may then be located by the proper moment equations from Arts. 39 and 40.

Example 1

Locate the centroid of the shaded area shown in Fig. 194.

Fig. 194.

Solution: The shaded area may be subdivided into a rectangle A_1, a triangle A_2, and a semicircle A_3. For convenience, the coordinate axes are placed as shown. The data for the various parts are as follows:

$$A_1 = 4 \times 8 = 32 \qquad x_1 = -2 \qquad y_1 = 4$$
$$A_2 = 3 \times 8/2 = 12 \qquad x_2 = -5 \qquad y_2 = 8/3$$
$$A_3 = -\pi(3)^2/2 = -14.1 \qquad x_3 = -4 \times 3/3\pi \qquad y_3 = 4$$
$$A = A_1 + A_2 + A_3 = 29.9$$

The moment equations may now be written:

$$\bar{x} = \frac{A_1x_1 + A_2x_2 + A_3x_3}{A} = \frac{(32)(-2) + (12)(-5) + (-9\pi/2)(-4 \times 3/3\pi)}{29.9}$$

$$= -3.54 \text{ in.}$$

$$\bar{y} = \frac{A_1y_1 + A_2y_2 + A_3y_3}{A} = \frac{(32)(4) + (12)(8/3) + (-9\pi/2)(4)}{29.9}$$

$$= +3.46 \text{ in.}$$

Example 2

Locate the centroid of the hollow conical frustum shown in Fig. 195 (a).

Solution: The frustum is extended to show the original cone of which it was a part as shown in Fig. 195 (b). It is now seen that the hollow

(a)   (b)

FIG. 195.

frustum may be considered as a cone V_1 of 15-ft. altitude and 6-ft. base diameter, from which have been taken a smaller cone V_2 of 10-ft. altitude and 4-ft. base diameter, and a cylinder V_3 of 5-ft. altitude and 2-ft. diameter. Coordinate axes are chosen as shown, so that $\bar{x} = \bar{z} = 0$. By moments with respect to the x axis:

$$\bar{y} = \frac{V_1 y_1 + V_2 y_2 + V_3 y_3}{V}$$

$$= \frac{[\frac{1}{3}\pi(3)^2(15)]\,[15/4] + [-\frac{1}{3}\pi(2)^2(10)]\,[10/4+5] + [-\pi(1)^2(5)]\,[5/2]}{[\frac{1}{3}\pi(3)^2(15)] - [\frac{1}{3}\pi(2)^2(10)] - [\pi(1)^2(5)]}$$

$$= 2.11 \text{ ft. above the bottom}$$

Problems

1. Locate the centroid of the T section shown in Fig. 196.

Ans. $\bar{y} = -0.714$ in.

2. A uniform wire 24 in. long is bent to form a right-angle triangle with legs 6 in. and 8 in. long. Locate the center of gravity of the wire.

Ans. 2 in. from the 8-in. leg; 3 in. from the 6-in. leg.

FIG. 196.

FIG. 197.

3. A steel cylinder 6 in. in diameter and 10 in. long has a concentric hole of 4-in. diameter bored through half its length. Locate the center of gravity.

Ans. 5.71 in. from the hollow end.

4. Solve Prob. 3 if the hole is filled with lead. Steel weighs 490 lb. per cu. ft.; lead weighs 710 lb. per cu. ft.   Ans. 4.77 in. in from the leaded end.

5. Locate the centroid of the area shown in Fig. 197.

Ans. $\bar{x} = 3.08$ in.; $\bar{y} = 1.70$ in.

FIG. 198.

6. The section shown in Fig. 198 is that of a standard 15-in. 33.9-lb. structural-steel channel. Locate its centroid, neglecting fillets and rounded corners.   Ans. $\bar{y} = 0.79$ in.

Art. 44. Surfaces and Solids of Revolution.   A surface of revolution is one generated by the rotation of a line about a non-inter-

secting axis.   In Fig. 199, the line AB of length l is rotated about the x axis, thus generating a surface of revolution.   Let point C be the centroid of the line and dl any differential portion of the line. By rotation of dl about the x axis, a surface is generated whose area is

$$dA = 2\pi y \, dl$$

The area of the entire surface of revolution is then

$$A = \int dA = \int 2\pi y \, dl = 2\pi \int y \, dl = 2\pi \bar{y} l$$

FIG. 199.   FIG. 200.

It is thus shown that the area of a surface of revolution is the product of the length of the generating line and the length of the path traced by the centroid of the line.

A solid of revolution is one generated by the rotation of an area about a non-intersecting axis.   In Fig. 200, the area A is rotated about the x axis, thus generating a solid of revolution.   Let point C be the centroid of the area and dA any differential portion of the area.   By rotating dA about the x axis, a differential solid is generated whose volume is

$$dV = 2\pi y \, dA$$

The volume of the entire solid of revolution is

$$V = \int dV = \int 2\pi y \, dA = 2\pi \int y \, dA = 2\pi \, \bar{y} A$$

Thus it is shown that the volume of a solid of revolution is the product of the generating area and the length of the path traced by the centroid of the area.

The two results thus developed are known as the theorems of Pappus and Guldinus.   Their advantage in determining the surface areas or volumes of solids of revolution lies in the fact that by their use integration may be avoided.

Example

The cross section of the rim of a flywheel of 20-in. radius is shown by
the shaded area in Fig. 201. Deter-
mine the weight of the rim if the
material is cast iron, weighing 450 lb.
per cu. ft.

Solution: The cross section of the
rim will be considered as a rectangle
from which a semicircle is cut out.

The volume generated by the rotation of the rectangle about the axis
of the wheel is

$$V_1 = 2\pi \bar{y} A = 2\pi \times 17 \times 72$$
$$= 7695 \text{ cu. in.}$$

Fig. 201.

The volume generated by rotation of the semicircle about the axis of
the wheel is

$$V_2 = 2\pi \bar{y} A = 2\pi \times \left(20 - \frac{4 \times 4}{3\pi}\right) \times \frac{\pi(4)^2}{2} = 2890 \text{ cu. in.}$$

The volume of the rim is thus

$$V = 7695 - 2890 = 4805 \text{ cu. in.} = 2.78 \text{ cu. ft.}$$

Its weight is

$$W = 2.78 \times 450 = 1250 \text{ lb.}$$

Problems

1. By the theorems of this article, determine the curved surface area and
volume of a cone of radius r, altitude h, and slant height s.

$$Ans. \quad A = \pi r s; \quad V = \tfrac{1}{3}\pi r^2 h.$$

2. Show by means of the first theorem that the surface area of a sphere
is $4\pi r^2$.

3. Given the volume of a sphere $= \tfrac{4}{3}\pi r^3$, show by means of the second
theorem that the centroidal distance of the area of a semicircle is $4r/3\pi$.

Fig. 202.

4. Determine the surface area and volume of the torus shown in Fig. 202.

$$Ans. \quad A = 197 \text{ sq. in.}; \quad V = 98.7 \text{ cu. in.}$$

Supplementary Problems

1. Locate the centroid of the structural-steel angle section shown in Fig. 203.   Neglect fillet and rounded corners.

Ans. $\bar{x} = 1.65$ in.; $\bar{y} = 2.65$ in.

2. A wire is bent into the form of a semicircular arc and its chord.   Locate the center of gravity.

Ans. 0.389r from center.

3. Locate the center of gravity of one quadrant of the ellipse, $x^2/a^2 + y^2/b^2 = 1$.

Ans. $\bar{x} = 4a/3\pi$; $\bar{y} = 4b/3\pi$.

4. Using the result of Prob. 3, determine the volume of the solid of revolution obtained by rotating the area of Prob. 3 about the x axis.

Ans. $V = \frac{2}{3}\pi ab^2$.

Fig. 203.

5. Locate the centroid of the solid of revolution in Prob. 4.   *Ans.* $\bar{x} = \frac{3}{8}a$.

6. Locate the centroid of the area shown in Fig. 204.

Ans. $\bar{x} = -6.44$ in.; $\bar{y} = 2.8$ in.

7. A hemispherical bowl has 12-in. outside radius and 10-in. inside radius. Determine the distance of the centroid from the geometric center.   Compare with the approximate result obtained by substituting the mean radius of the bowl in the answer to Prob. 4, Art. 42.

Ans. 5.53 in.; 5.50 in.

8. The cross section of the rim of a cable wheel of 2-ft. diameter is shown in Fig. 205.   Determine the volume of the rim.

Ans. 750 cu. in.

Fig. 204.

9. Locate the center of gravity of a pole 12 in. in diameter at the bottom, 4 in. in diameter at the top, and 30 ft. high.   *Ans.* 10.4 ft. from the bottom.

Fig. 205.

Fig. 206.

10. A thin-walled cylindrical tank with hemispherical bottom has dimensions as shown in Fig. 206.   Determine the distance of the center of gravity of the empty tank from the top.   *Ans.* 3.5 ft.

11. If the tank of Prob. 10 is full of water determine the distance of the center of gravity of the water from the top.   *Ans.* 3.04 ft.

12. The cross section of a girder consisting of a plate riveted to an I-beam is shown in Fig. 207. The area of the I-beam is 12.49 sq. in. Determine $\bar{y}$ of the section. (Disregard the rivets.)   *Ans.* $\bar{y} = 9.38$ in.

13. Fig. 208 shows the cross section of a crane-runway girder consisting of a 15-in. 33.9-lb. channel riveted to a 30-in. 116-lb. Carnegie beam. The area

Fig. 207.

Fig. 208.

of the channel is 9.90 sq. in., and its centroid is 0.79 in. from the outside of the web. The area of the CB section is 34.13 sq. in. Locate the centroid of the girder section.   *Ans.* $\bar{y} = 18.3$ in.

14. The T-section shown in Fig. 209 is composed of two 12-in. by $\frac{1}{2}$-in. plates and two 5-in. by $3\frac{1}{2}$-in. by $\frac{3}{8}$-in. angles. The distance of the centroid of one angle section from the 5-in. leg is 0.86 in., and the area is 3.05 sq. in. Compute $\bar{y}$.   *Ans.* 9.97 in.

Fig. 209.

CHAPTER VII

MOMENT OF INERTIA

Art. 45. Moment of Inertia and Radius of Gyration of Area. In the development of certain topics in the mechanics of materials, integral quantities of the form $\int x^2 dA$, $\int y^2 dA$, and $\int \rho^2 dA$ arise and form a part of important and frequently used engineering formulas. In these expressions dA represents a differential element of an area A, as shown in Fig. 210; x and y represent the distances of the element from rectangular axes in the plane of the area; and ρ represents the distance from a polar axis or axis perpendicular to the plane of the area. Since such mathematical expressions occur so frequently, it is desirable to designate them by some name and symbol, and to evaluate them for certain commonly occurring areas. The name *moment of inertia of area* has been given to these quantities because they resemble in form the expression $\int r^2 dM$ which is later defined as the moment of inertia of mass. Since

FIG. 210.

area possesses no inertia, the term moment of inertia of area is somewhat inaccurate, and the term *second moment of area* would be preferable. However, through long usage, the term moment of inertia has become conventional and universally accepted.

The moment of inertia of an area about an axis in its plane is called the rectangular moment of inertia and is denoted by I. Thus, the moment of inertia of the area A in Fig. 210 with respect to the x axis is given by

$$I_x = \int y^2 dA$$

Similarly

$$I_y = \int x^2 dA$$

118

The moment of inertia of an area with respect to an axis perpendicular to its plane is called the polar moment of inertia and is denoted by J.   Thus, the polar moment of inertia of the area A in Fig. 210 with respect to a z axis passing through O and normal to the x–y plane is given by

$$J = \int \rho^2 dA$$

Since it always involves the product of area and square of distance, the moment of inertia of an area is expressed in terms of some unit of length raised to the fourth power and is essentially positive.   In most cases the inch is the unit of length used, and the moment of inertia is expressed in inches to the fourth power, written $in.^4$ It is again emphasized that moment of inertia of area is purely a mathematical concept; it has no physical basis and cannot be illustrated by diagram or other graphic representation.

The distance k, which when squared and multiplied by an area equals the moment of inertia of the area, is called the *radius of gyration* of the area.   Thus

$$I = k^2 \cdot A$$

$$k = \sqrt{\frac{I}{A}}$$

Radius of gyration may also be defined as the distance from the axis of inertia at which the entire area could be concentrated and still possess the same moment of inertia as in its actually distributed form.   Care should be taken not to confuse radius of gyration k with centroidal distance $\bar{y}$ which was discussed in the preceding chapter.

Art. 46. Moment of Inertia of Area by Integration.   The algebraic expressions for the moments of inertia of some of the more common and basic forms of area will now be determined by means of the calculus.   In setting up the required integral, the element of area dA may be selected in various ways.   Either cartesian or polar coordinates may be used and either single or double integration may result, depending on how the element of area is selected.   Certain precautions, however, must be observed in selecting the element of area so that it will conform to one of the following rules:

1. All points in the element should be equally distant from the inertia axis, otherwise the distance x, y, or ρ would be indefi-

nite.   Since these distances are squared, the average distance cannot be used.

2. The element is of such form and so located that its moment
of inertia with respect to the reference axis is already known.   The
moment of inertia of the area is then obtained by summing up the
moments of inertia of all the elements.

Example 1

By integration determine the moment of inertia and radius of gyration
of a rectangle in terms of its base b and altitude d,
with respect to an axis through its base.

FIG. 211.

Solution: The differential element of area dA,
selected according to the first rule, is $b\,dy$, as
shown in Fig. 211.

$$I_x = \int y^2 dA = \int_0^d y^2 \cdot b\,dy = b \int_0^d y^2 dy$$

$$I_x = \frac{bd^3}{3}$$

$$k_x = \sqrt{\frac{I_x}{A}} = \sqrt{\frac{bd^3}{3bd}} = \frac{d}{\sqrt{3}}$$

Example 2

Derive the expression for the moment of inertia and radius of gyration
of a triangle of base b and altitude d with
respect to an axis through the vertex parallel
to the base.

Solution: The element of area, selected in
accordance with the first rule, is $u\,dy$, as shown
in Fig. 212.

$$I_x = \int y^2 dA = \int y^2 \cdot u\,dy$$

By similar triangles

FIG. 212.

$$\frac{u}{b} = \frac{y}{d} \quad \text{or} \quad u = \frac{b}{d} \cdot y$$

$$I_x = \int y^2 \cdot \frac{b}{d} \cdot y\,dy = \frac{b}{d} \int_0^d y^3\,dy$$

$$I_x = \frac{bd^3}{4}$$

$$k_x = \sqrt{\frac{I_x}{A}} = \sqrt{\frac{bd^3}{4} \cdot \frac{2}{bd}} = \frac{d}{\sqrt{2}}$$

Example 3

Derive the expression for the moment of inertia and radius of gyration of the area of a circle of radius r with respect to a diameter.

Solution: If polar coordinates are employed, the differential area, selected according to the first rule, is $\rho d\theta d\rho$, as shown in Fig. 213.

$$I_x = \int y^2 dA$$

From Fig. 213,

$$y = \rho \sin \theta$$

Fig. 213.

$$I_x = \iint \rho^2 \sin^2 \theta \cdot \rho d\theta d\rho = \int_0^{2\pi} \int_0^r \rho^3 d\rho \cdot \sin^2 \theta d\theta$$

$$I_x = \frac{r^4}{4} \int_0^{2\pi} \frac{(1 - \cos 2\theta)}{2} \, d\theta = \frac{r^4}{4} \left[\frac{\theta}{2} - \frac{\sin 2\theta}{4} \right]_0^{2\pi}$$

$$I_x = \frac{\pi r^4}{4}$$

$$k_x = \sqrt{\frac{I_x}{A}} = \sqrt{\frac{\pi r^4}{4\pi r^2}} = \frac{r}{2}$$

Example 4

Determine the polar moment of inertia and radius of gyration of the area of a circle of radius r with respect to an axis through its center.

Solution: The differential area, selected in accordance with the first rule is $2\pi \rho d\rho$, as shown in Fig. 214.

$$J = \int \rho^2 dA$$

$$J = \int \rho^2 2\pi \rho d\rho = 2\pi \int_0^r \rho^3 d\rho$$

Fig. 214.

$$J = \pi r^4 / 2$$

$$k = \sqrt{\frac{J}{A}} = \sqrt{\frac{\pi r^4}{2\pi r^2}} = \frac{r}{\sqrt{2}}$$

Example 5

Determine the moment of inertia, with respect to the x axis, of the area of the parabolic half-segment of base a and altitude b, shown in Fig. 215. The equation of the parabola is $y^2 = mx$.

FIG. 215.

Solution: Although the element of area could be selected in accordance with the first rule, an opportunity is afforded here to illustrate the use of the second rule. Accordingly, the element is taken as a rectangle whose base is on the x axis. From the result of Ex. 1 of this article, the moment of inertia of the element with respect to the x axis is

$$dI_x = \frac{dx \cdot y^3}{3}$$

The moment of inertia of the entire area is now obtained by summing up the moments of inertia of the elements.

$$I_x = \int dI_x = \int \tfrac{1}{3} y^3 \, dx$$

From the equation of the parabola, $y = m^{1/2} x^{1/2}$. By substitution of the dimensions a and b into the equation of the parabola, $m = b^2/a$, and thus

$$y = \frac{b}{a^{1/2}} \cdot x^{1/2}$$

$$I_x = \int_0^a \frac{1}{3} \frac{b^3}{a^{3/2}} x^{3/2} dx = \frac{b^3}{3a^{3/2}} \int_0^a x^{3/2} dx$$

$$I_x = \tfrac{2}{15} ab^3$$

Problems

1. Determine the moment of inertia of a rectangle with respect to a centroidal axis parallel to the base.   *Ans.* $bd^3/12$.

2. Derive the expression for the moment of inertia of a triangle with respect to an axis through its base.   *Ans.* $bd^3/12$.

3. Derive the expression for the moment of inertia of a triangle with respect to a centroidal axis parallel to its base.   *Ans.* $bd^3/36$.

4. Determine the polar moment of inertia of a square of side b with respect to an axis through its center.   *Ans.* $b^4/6$.

5. Determine I_x for the ellipse whose equation is $x^2/a^2 + y^2/b^2 = 1$.

Ans. $\frac{1}{4}\,\pi ab^3$.

6. Solve Ex. 3 above, using cartesian coordinates.

7. Solve Ex. 4, using $dA = \rho d\theta d\rho$ as in Ex. 3.

8. Determine the moment of inertia with respect to the y axis of the area shown in Fig. 215.

Ans. $\frac{2}{7}\,a^3 b$.

Art. 47. Relation between Polar and Rectangular Moments of Inertia. In Fig. 216, the x and y axes lie in the plane of the area and a polar axis passes through 0. By definition,

$$J_O = \int \rho^2 dA$$

In the figure,

$$\rho^2 = x^2 + y^2$$

$$J_O = \int (x^2 + y^2)dA = \int x^2 dA + \int y^2 dA$$

FIG. 216.

Since, by definition

$$\int x^2 dA = I_y \quad \text{and} \quad \int y^2 dA = I_x,$$

$$\mathbf{J_O = I_y + I_x}$$

The moment of inertia of an area with respect to any polar axis is equal to the sum of its moments of inertia with respect to any two rectangular axes in its plane which intersect on the polar axis.

Problems

1. Verify the above theorem, using the results of Ex. 3 and 4 of Art. 46.

FIG. 217.

2. Compute the moment of inertia of the rectangle shown in Fig. 217 with respect to a polar axis through its centroid C. *Ans.* $J_C = 104$ in.^{4}

3. Assuming the result obtained in Prob. 5, Art. 46, determine the moment of inertia of the ellipse with respect to a polar axis through its centroid.

$$\text{Ans. } J_C = \frac{\pi ab}{4}\,(a^2 + b^2).$$

4. Solve Prob. 4, Art. 46, by means of the theorem of this article.

5. By means of symmetry and the theorem of this article, show that the moment of inertia of a square is the same with respect to any centroidal axis in its plane.

Art. 48. Relation between Moments of Inertia of Area with Respect to Parallel Axes. If the moment of inertia of an area with

FIG. 218.

respect to a centroidal axis in its plane is known, the moment of inertia with respect to any other parallel axis may be obtained without integration. In Fig. 218, gx represents the centroidal or "gravity" axis for the area shown, and x_1 represents any other parallel axis at distance d from the gx axis. By definition,

$$I_{x_1} = \int y_1{}^2 dA = \int (y + d)^2 dA$$

$$= \int (y^2 + 2yd + d^2) dA$$

$$= \int y^2 dA + d^2 \int dA + 2d \int y dA$$

By definition,

$$\int y^2 dA = I_{gx}$$

$$d^2 \int dA = Ad^2$$

$$2d \int y dA = 2d \cdot \bar{y} \cdot A$$

Since gx is a centroidal axis, $\bar{y} = 0$ and the last term drops out. The expression for I_{x_1} then becomes

$$\mathbf{I_{x_1} = I_{gx} + Ad^2}$$

It is evident from the above result that the moment of inertia of an area with respect to any axis in its plane is equal to its moment of inertia about a parallel centroidal axis plus the product of the area and the square of the distance between the two axes. This statement is known as the *transfer formula* or *parallel-axis theorem*.

It should be noted from the above statement that the moment of inertia of an area will always be less about a centroidal axis than about any other parallel axis. *It should also be noted that one of the two axes involved in the equation must be centroidal.* Hence, in transferring the moment of inertia of an area from one to the other of two parallel axes, it is always necessary for one of the axes to be taken through the centroid.   If it is desired to transfer the moment of inertia of an area from one axis to another when neither axis is centroidal, the operation may be accomplished in two steps, the moment of inertia about the centroidal axis being an intermediate result.

Example 1

Given $I = bd^3/4$ for a triangle with respect to an axis through the vertex parallel to the base (see Ex. 2, Art. 46), determine without further integration the moment of inertia with respect to an axis through the base.

FIG. 219.

Solution: The triangle is shown in Fig. 219 in which x_1 is the axis through the vertex and x_2 is the axis through the base.   Since neither x_1 nor x_2 is a centroidal axis, the transfer must be made in two steps, that is from x_1 to the centroidal axis gx, and then from gx to x_2.

$$I_{x_1} = I_{gx} + Ad^2$$

$$\frac{bd^3}{4} = I_{gx} + \left(\frac{bd}{2}\right)\left(\frac{2d}{3}\right)^2$$

$$I_{gx} = \frac{bd^3}{36}$$

Then

$$I_{x_2} = I_{gx} + Ad^2 = \frac{bd^3}{36} + \left(\frac{bd}{2}\right)\left(\frac{d}{3}\right)^2 = \frac{bd^3}{12}$$

FIG. 220.

Example 2

Compute by means of the transfer formula the moment of inertia of a semi-circle of 10-in. radius with respect to a tangent axis x_2 parallel to its bounding diameter, as shown in Fig. 220.

Solution: From Ex. 3, Art. 46,

$$I_{x_1} = \frac{\pi r^4}{8} = \frac{\pi (10)^4}{8} = 3930 \text{ in.}^4$$

$$\bar{y} = \frac{4r}{3\pi} = \frac{4 \times 10}{3\pi} = 4.24 \text{ in.}$$

$$I_{x_1} = I_{gx} + Ad^2$$

$$3930 = I_{gx} + \frac{\pi(10)^2}{2}(4.24)^2$$

$$I_{gx} = 1110 \text{ in.}^4$$

Then

$$I_{x_2} = I_{gx} + Ad^2 = 1110 + \frac{\pi(10)^2}{2}(10 - 4.24)^2 = 6330 \text{ in.}^4$$

Problems

1. Derive the transfer formula for polar moment of inertia. Hint: In Fig. 221, $J_O = \int \rho_1^2 dA$ and $\rho_1^2 = (a + x)^2 + (y - b)^2$. *Ans.* $J_O = J_C + Ad^2$.

FIG. 221.   FIG. 222.

2. Compute the moment of inertia of the triangle shown in Fig. 222 with respect to the x_1 axis.   *Ans.* 6780 in.^{4}

3. Determine the moment of inertia of the rectangle in Fig. 223 with respect to the y_1 axis.   *Ans.* 2770 in.^{4}

4. Determine the moment of inertia of the rectangle in Fig. 223 with respect to a polar axis through O.   *Ans.* 2860 in.^{4}

FIG. 223.   FIG. 224.

5. Compute the moment of inertia of the area of the quadrant shown in Fig. 224 with respect to the x_1 axis.   *Ans.* 225 in.^{4}

6. Determine the moment of inertia of the area of a circle of 6-in. diameter with respect to a polar axis through its circumference.   *Ans.* 382 in.^{4}

Art. 49. Moment of Inertia of Composite Areas.   If an area consists of a combination of two or more simple areas, such as rectangles, triangles, and portions of circles, for which the moments of inertia are known, the moment of inertia of the entire area may be obtained by adding the moments of inertia of the component parts.   If a component area represents a portion to be removed, its moment of inertia is, of course, subtracted.

In order to combine moments of inertia of component areas it is necessary that they all be taken with reference to the same axis.   The transfer formula should be used as needed.

Example 1

Locate the centroidal axis 1–1 of the T-section shown in Fig. 225, and compute the moment of inertia of the area with respect to this axis.

Fig. 225.

Solution: First Method.   The centroid is located with respect to the x axis by means of the equation

$$A\bar{y} = A_1 y_1 + A_2 y_2$$

$$48\bar{y} = 24 \times 1 + 24(-6)$$

$$\bar{y} = -2.5 \text{ in.}$$

The moment of inertia of the upper rectangle is determined about its own centroidal axis and transferred to the 1–1 axis as follows,

$$I_{1-1} = I_{gx} + Ad^2 = \frac{12(2)^3}{12} + 24(3.5)^2 = 302 \text{ in.}^4$$

For the lower rectangle

$$I_{1-1} = \frac{2(12)^3}{12} + 24(3.5)^2 = 582 \text{ in.}^4$$

The moment of inertia of the entire T-section is

$$I_{1-1} = 302 + 582 = 884 \text{ in.}^4$$

Second Method.   A simpler solution is possible when all component areas have a common boundary line.   The x-axis is a common boundary in this case.   The moment of inertia of the entire area about the x axis is first obtained and then transferred to the 1–1 axis.

$$I_x = \frac{12(2)^3}{3} + \frac{2(12)^3}{3} = 1184 \text{ in.}^4$$

$$I_{1-1} = I_x - Ad^2 = 1184 - 48(2.5)^2 = 884 \text{ in.}^4$$

Example 2

Determine the moment of inertia of the I-section shown in Fig. 226 with respect to the centroidal axis 1–1.

FIG. 226.

Solution: First Method. Since the 1–1 axis is also centroidal for the central rectangle, its moment of inertia is

$$I_{1-1} = \frac{2(6)^3}{12} = 36 \text{ in.}^4$$

The value of I_{1-1} for either upper or lower rectangle is obtained by transfer,

$$I_{1-1} = I_{gx} + Ad^2 = \frac{6(2)^3}{12} + 12(4)^2 = 196 \text{ in.}^4$$

Then,

$$\text{total } I_{1-1} = 36 + 2(196) = 428 \text{ in.}^4$$

Second Method. The moment of inertia of this section may also be determined without transfer by considering the section as a 6-in. by 10-in. rectangle from which a 4-in. by 6-in. rectangle is subtracted, the 1–1 axis being centroidal for each.

$$I_{1-1} = \frac{6(10)^3}{12} - \frac{4(6)^3}{12} = 428 \text{ in.}^4$$

It is evident from the preceding examples that the moment of inertia of a given composite area may sometimes be obtained by several methods which may differ considerably in the amount of computation involved. No single rule can be stated which will indicate in all cases the most convenient method to adopt. Each problem must be considered individually.

Problems

1. Compute the moment of inertia and radius of gyration of a hollow circular section of 6-in. outside diameter and 4-in. inside diameter with respect to an axis in its plane through the center. *Ans.* 51 in.^{4}; 1.8 in.

2. A box column is made up of four 2-in. by 6-in. timbers fastened together as shown in Fig. 227. Determine the moment of inertia and radius of gyration of the section with respect to the centroidal axis 1–1. *Ans.* 320 in.^{4}; 2.58 in.

FIG. 227.

3. Determine the moment of inertia of the American standard 15-in. 33.9-lb. channel section in Fig. 228 with respect to the 1–1 axis.

Ans. 313 in.^{4}

4. Locate the 2–2 axis of the channel section in Fig. 228, and determine the moment of inertia about this axis.   *Ans.* $\bar{x} = 0.79$ in.; $I_{2-2} = 8.2$ in.[4]

FIG. 228.   FIG. 229.

5. Determine the moment of inertia of the area shown in Fig. 229 with respect to the x axis.   *Ans.* 530 in.[4]

6. Determine the moment of inertia of the area shown in Fig. 230 with respect to the gx axis.   *Ans.* 74.4 in.[4] ($\bar{y} = 3.22$ in.)

7. Determine the moment of inertia of the area shown in Fig. 230 with respect to the gy axis.   *Ans.* 171 in.[4]

FIG. 230.

FIG. 231.

8. The cross section of a structural steel column composed of two 15-in. 40-lb. channels and two 18-in. by 1-in. plates is shown in Fig. 231 (*a*). For one channel, shown in Fig. 231 (*b*), $A = 11.7$ sq. in., $I_{1-1} = 346$, $I_{2-2} = 9.3$, and $\bar{x} = 0.78$ in. Determine the moment of inertia and radius of gyration of the section with respect to each of the axes 1–1 and 2–2.

Ans. $I_{1-1} = 3000$ in.[4]; $k_{1-1} = 7.10$ in.
$I_{2-2} = 1770$ in.[4]; $k_{2-2} = 5.45$ in.

Art. 50. Principal Axes of Inertia. Except for a few special cases, the moment of inertia of an area is not the same with respect to all axes in its plane passing through a given point. It can be shown, however, that there are two axes 90° apart for which the moments of inertia of the area are greater and less, respectively, than for any other axes through the point. These are called the principal axes of inertia of the area. It can further be shown that axes of symmetry are principal axes.

In the solution of many problems in the mechanics of materials, the moment of inertia of an area must be determined with respect to a principal axis through its centroid. In the rectangle, Fig. 232, the centroidal principal axes are the axes of symmetry, 1–1 and

Fig. 232.   Fig. 233.

2–2. If the vertical dimension is the larger, then the moment of inertia of the rectangle with respect to axis 1–1 is the maximum moment of inertia and that with respect to axis 2–2 is the minimum. In the equal-angle section, Fig. 233, the axes 3–3 and 4–4 are the centroidal principal axes and are inclined at 45° with axes 1–1 and 2–2. The moment of inertia with respect to axis 4–4 is the maximum.

Supplementary Problems

Fig. 234.

1. Compute the moment of inertia and radius of gyration of the area shown in Fig. 234 with respect to the gx axis.   *Ans.* 5.97 in.⁴; 1.01 in.

2. Compute the moment of inertia and radius of gyration of the area shown in Fig. 234 with respect to a polar axis through the geometric center.
Ans. 11.9 in.⁴; 1.43 in.

3. For the structural-steel angle section shown in Fig. 235, $\bar{x} = 1.65$ in.

and $\bar{y} = 2.65$ in.   Neglecting fillets and rounded corners, determine the moments of inertia with respect to the centroidal axes 1–1 and 2–2.

Ans. 80.8 in.[4]; 38.8 in.[4]

FIG. 235.

FIG. 236.

4. The cross section of a 10-in. 49-lb. Carnegie beam is shown in Fig. 236. Determine the moments of inertia of the area with respect to the axes 1–1 and 2–2.   *Ans.* 273 in.[4]; 93.0 in.[4]

5. Locate the gx axis of the area shown in Fig. 237 and compute the moments of inertia of the area with respect to the axes gx and gy.

Ans. $\bar{y} = 3.22$ in.; $I_{gx} = 82.1$ in.[4]; $I_{gy} = 408$ in.[4]

FIG. 237.

6. Locate the gx axis of the T-section shown in Fig. 238, and compute the moment of inertia with respect to this axis.

Ans. $\bar{y} = 7.98$ in.; $I_{gx} = 645$ in.[4]

FIG. 238.

FIG. 239.

7. Compute the moments of inertia of the area shown in Fig. 239 with respect to the x and y axes.   *Ans.* 603 in.[4]; 198 in.[4]

8. The section shown in Fig. 240 (*a*) consists of four 6-in. by 4-in. by $\frac{1}{2}$-in. angles and one 12-in. by $\frac{1}{2}$-in. web plate. The 4-in. legs of the angles are attached to the web plate. The data for one angle are given in Fig. 240 (*b*). Compute the moments of inertia of the section with respect to axes 1–1 and 2–2. *Ans.* 623 in.⁴; 165 in.⁴

Fig. 240.

9. Solve Prob. 8 if two 14-in. by $\frac{1}{2}$-in. flange plates are added, one on the top and one on the bottom. *Ans.* 1220 in.⁴; 394 in.⁴

Fig. 241.

10. The latticed channel section shown in Fig. 241 (*a*) consists of two 10-in. 20-lb. channels. The data for one channel are given in Fig. 241 (*b*). Compute the back-to-back distance *d* to make $I_{1-1} = I_{2-2}$. *Ans.* 5.96 in.

Art. 51. Moment of Inertia and Radius of Gyration of Mass.

It will be shown in a subsequent chapter that a rotating body tends to resist any change in its motion and that any such change produced by external actions depends inversely on a property of the rotating body known as its *moment of inertia*. Experience has shown that the resistance offered depends on the amount of mass involved and the square of its distance from the axis.   Hence the moment of inertia of a body is expressed in terms of mass and square of distance.   For a particle of mass dM located at distance ρ from the axis of rotation the moment of inertia is $\rho^2 dM$.   The moment of inertia of a body is the summation of such expressions for all elements in the body and thus becomes the integral $\int \rho^2 dM$ which will be represented by I.

In evaluating the above integral, it is often convenient to make use of the relation between mass, volume, and density γ.   If γ is constant,

$$M = \gamma V \quad \text{and} \quad dM = \gamma \cdot dV$$

$$I = \int \rho^2 dM = \gamma \int \rho^2 dV$$

The *radius of gyration* of a mass, denoted by k, may be defined as the distance from the axis at which the entire mass may be concentrated and still have the same moment of inertia as it has in its actually distributed form.   Thus,

$$\mathbf{I = Mk^2} \quad \text{or} \quad \mathbf{k = \sqrt{\frac{I}{M}}}$$

It will be shown later that the unit of mass used in engineering is one possessing g units of weight, where g represents the acceleration of gravity in feet per second per second.   Thus $M = W/g$.   If distances are also expressed in feet, then the units entering into moment of inertia of mass are:

$$\frac{\text{lb.}}{\text{ft./sec.}^2} \times \text{ft.}^2 = \text{lb.} \times \text{sec.}^2 \times \text{ft.}$$

There is no generally accepted name for the unit of moment of inertia of mass, and usually no units are specified.   It will be assumed in subsequent problems that the numerical results are to be determined in terms of the engineering units as explained above.

Art. 52. Moment of Inertia of Mass by Integration.   The algebraic expressions for the moments of inertia of some of the more frequently occurring forms of rotating mass will now be determined by means of the calculus.   In setting up the required integral, the differential element may be selected in various ways.   Either cartesian or polar coordinates may be used, and either single, double, or triple integration may result, depending on how the element is selected. The element should be selected in accordance with one of the following rules.

1. All points in the element should be equally distant from the reference axis, otherwise the distance ρ would be indefinite. Since these distances are squared, the average distance cannot be used.

2. The element is of such form and so located that its moment of inertia with respect to the reference axis is already known. The moment of inertia of the mass is then obtained by summing up the moments of inertia of all elements.

FIG. 242.

Example 1

Derive the expressions for the moment of inertia of a right prism having any shape cross section with respect to any axis perpendicular to the bases.

Solution: The right prism of altitude h is shown in Fig. 242. The y axis is perpendicular to the bases. A differential area dA is extended from the upper to the lower base thus forming the differential volume $dV = h \cdot dA$. The element of mass is then $\gamma dV = \gamma h dA$ and conforms to the first rule stated above.

$$I_y = \int \rho^2 dM = \int \rho^2 \gamma h dA = \gamma h \int \rho^2 dA$$

The quantity $\int \rho^2 dA$ is the polar moment of inertia J of the base with respect to the y axis; hence

$$I_y = \gamma \cdot h \cdot J$$

The above result holds for any right prism, and from it may be derived the expressions for any special case.

Case 1. Right circular cylinder with respect to geometric axis. Here the base of the prism is a circle of radius r whose polar moment of inertia about the axis through its center is $J = \pi r^4/2$. Hence

$$I_y = \gamma \cdot h \cdot \frac{\pi r^4}{2} = \frac{1}{2} r^2 \cdot (\gamma \pi r^2 h) = \frac{1}{2} M r^2$$

$$k_y = \sqrt{\frac{I_y}{M}} = \sqrt{\frac{1}{2} r^2} = \frac{r}{\sqrt{2}}$$

Case 2. Rectangular prism of sides a, b, and h with respect to a geometric axis parallel to side h. Here the base is a rectangle of sides a and b as shown in Fig. 243. For the base,

$$J = I_x + I_z = \frac{ab^3}{12} + \frac{ba^3}{12} = \frac{ab}{12}(b^2 + a^2)$$

For the mass,

$$I_y = \gamma h \cdot J = \frac{\gamma h\, ab}{12}(b^2 + a^2) = \frac{1}{12}(a^2 + b^2)(\gamma abh) = \frac{1}{12}M(a^2 + b^2)$$

$$k_y = \sqrt{\frac{I_y}{M}} = \sqrt{\frac{a^2 + b^2}{12}}$$

FIG. 243.

FIG. 244.

Example 2

Derive the expression for the moment of inertia and radius of gyration of a sphere with respect to a geometric axis.

Solution: A sphere of radius r is shown in Fig. 244, the y axis being a geometric axis. It is convenient in this example to make use of the second rule in selecting the differential element. The element is accordingly taken as a circular plate of radius x and thickness dy. From Ex. 1, the moment of inertia of the element is

$$dI_y = \tfrac{1}{2} dM \cdot x^2 = \tfrac{1}{2}\gamma \pi x^2 dy \cdot x^2$$

The moment of inertia of the sphere is the sum of the moments of inertia of the elements.

$$I_y = \int dI_y = \tfrac{1}{2}\gamma\pi \int x^4 dy$$

Since

$$x^2 = r^2 - y^2$$

$$I_y = \tfrac{1}{2}\gamma\pi \int_{-r}^{+r} (r^2 - y^2)^2 dy$$

$$I_y = \gamma\pi \int_0^r (r^4 - 2r^2y^2 + y^4)dy$$

$$= \tfrac{8}{15}\gamma\pi r^5$$

Since

$$M = \tfrac{4}{3}\gamma\pi r^3$$

$$I_y = \tfrac{2}{5}Mr^2$$

$$k_y = \sqrt{\frac{I_y}{M}} = r\sqrt{0.4}$$

Example 3

Derive the expressions for the moment of inertia and radius of gyration of a slender rod with respect to an axis normal to the rod through one end.

FIG. 245.

Solution: A rod of length l and cross sectional area A is shown in Fig. 245. The x axis is normal to the rod through the upper end. The mass of the differential element shown is $dM = \gamma dV = \gamma A d\rho$. It will be seen that all points in the element are not equally distant from the axis. If ρ is the distance of the center of the element from the x axis, then the distance of other points is slightly greater, particularly in elements lying near the axis. Thus the moment of inertia obtained by use of the element shown will be less than the true moment of inertia. The error involved decreases as the ratio of the length of the rod to the dimensions of the cross section increases. For a circular cylinder whose length is ten times the diameter the error is $\tfrac{3}{16}$ per cent.

$$I_x = \int \rho^2 dM = \gamma A \int_0^l \rho^2 d\rho = \frac{\gamma A l^3}{3}$$

Since

$$M = \gamma A l$$

$$I_x = \tfrac{1}{3}Ml^2$$

$$k_x = \sqrt{\frac{I}{M}} = \frac{l}{\sqrt{3}}$$

Problems

1. Derive the expression for the moment of inertia of a right circular cone of altitude h and radius of base r with respect to its geometric axis.

Ans. $\tfrac{3}{10}Mr^2$.

2. Derive the expression for the moment of inertia of a slender rod with respect to a centroidal axis normal to its length.   *Ans.* $\frac{1}{12} Ml^2$.

3. Derive the expression for the moment of inertia of a slender rod with respect to an axis through one end of the rod and at angle θ with its length.

$Ans.$ $\frac{1}{3} Ml^2 \sin^2 \theta$.

4. Derive the expression for the moment of inertia of a thin circular disk of radius r with respect to a centroidal diameter.   *Ans.* $\frac{1}{4} Mr^2$.

5. Derive the expression for the moment of inertia of a hollow right circular cylinder of outside radius r_1 and inside radius r_2 with respect to its geometric axis.   *Ans.* $\frac{1}{2} M(r_1{}^2 + r_2{}^2)$.

Art. 53. Relation between Moments of Inertia of Mass with Respect to Parallel Axes. It is often necessary to determine the moment of inertia of a mass with respect to some axis other than that for which the moment of inertia is already known. If the two axes are parallel and one is centroidal, a simple relation may be derived making it possible to transfer the moment of inertia from one axis to the other.

Fig. 246 represents a section through a body perpendicular to an axis through

Fig. 246.

the center of gravity C. A parallel axis at distance d from the centroidal axis passes through O. Let dM be any element of mass at distances ρ_1 from O and ρ from C. By definition,

$$I_O = \int \rho_1{}^2 dM$$

From the figure,

$$\rho_1{}^2 = (x + a)^2 + (y - b)^2$$

$$= x^2 + 2ax + a^2 + y^2 - 2by + b^2$$

$$= (x^2 + y^2) + (a^2 + b^2) + 2ax - 2by$$

$$= \rho^2 + d^2 + 2ax - 2by$$

$$I_O = \int (\rho^2 + d^2 + 2ax - 2by) dM$$

$$I_O = \int \rho^2 dM + d^2 \int dM + 2a \int x\, dM - 2b \int y\, dM$$

$$I_O = I_C + Md^2 + 2aM\bar{x} - 2bM\bar{y}$$

Since axes gx and gy are centroidal, $\bar{x} = 0$ and $\bar{y} = 0$. Thus

$$\mathbf{I_O = I_C + Md^2}$$

It is evident from the above result that the moment of inertia of a mass with respect to any axis is equal to the moment of inertia with respect to a parallel centroidal axis plus the product of the mass and the square of the distance between the two axes. This statement is known as the *transfer formula* or *parallel-axis theorem for masses*.

It will be noted from the above statement that the moment of inertia of a mass will always be less about a centroidal axis than about any other parallel axis. *It should also be noted that one of the two axes involved in the equation must be centroidal.* If it is desired to transfer the moment of inertia of a mass from one axis to another when neither axis is centroidal, the operation may be accomplished in two steps, the moment of inertia about the centroidal axis being an intermediate result.

Example

Derive the expression for the moment of inertia of a right circular cylinder of altitude h and radius of base r with respect to a diameter of the base.

FIG. 247.

Solution: The differential element is a circular disk of radius r and thickness dy, as shown in Fig. 247. From Prob. 4, Art. 52, the moment of inertia of the disk about its centroidal axis gx is

$$dI_{gx} = \tfrac{1}{4}dMr^2$$

By the transfer formula, the moment of inertia of the disk with respect to the parallel x axis is

$$dI_x = \tfrac{1}{4}dMr^2 + y^2 dM$$

The moment of inertia of the cylinder with respect to the x axis is

$$I_x = \int dI_x = \tfrac{1}{4}r^2 \int dM + \int y^2 dM$$

$$I_x = \tfrac{1}{4}r^2 \int_0^h \gamma \pi r^2 dy + \int_0^h y^2 \cdot \gamma \pi r^2 dy$$

$$I_x = M\left(\frac{r^2}{4} + \frac{h^2}{3}\right)$$

Problems

1. From the result of the preceding example determine, without further integration, the moment of inertia of the cylinder with respect to a centroidal axis parallel to the base.   *Ans.* $\tfrac{1}{4}M(r^2 + \tfrac{1}{3}h^2)$.

2. From the result of Ex. 2, Art. 52, determine, without further integration, the moment of inertia of a sphere with respect to a tangent.   *Ans.* $\tfrac{7}{5}Mr^2$.

3. From the result of Ex. 1, Art. 52, determine, without further integration, the moment of inertia of a right circular cylinder with respect to an element of the curved surface.   *Ans.* $\tfrac{3}{2}Mr^2$.

Art. 54. Computation of Moment of Inertia of Simple and Composite Masses.

As stated in Art. 51, the numerical value of the moment of inertia of a mass will be computed in terms of engineering units. All distances must therefore be expressed in feet, and the number of mass units is obtained by dividing weight in pounds by $g = 32.2$. Since the resulting unit of moment of inertia has no accepted name, the results will be stated as abstract numbers.

The moment of inertia of a composite mass about a given axis may be obtained by adding the moments of inertia of its component parts with respect to the same axis. The transfer formula should be used when needed.

Example

Determine the moment of inertia of a 6-in. diameter cast-iron governor ball with respect to an axis 8 in. from its center. Cast iron weighs 450 lb. per cu. ft.

Solution: The weight of the ball is

$$W = \tfrac{4}{3}\pi(\tfrac{3}{12})^3 \times 450 = 29.4 \text{ lb.}$$

Then

$$M = W/g = 29.4/32.2 = 0.915$$

By the transfer formula,

$$I_O = I_C + Md^2$$
$$= \tfrac{2}{5}Mr^2 + Md^2 = \tfrac{2}{5} \times .915 \times (3/12)^2 + .915 \times (8/12)^2$$
$$I_O = 0.43$$

Problems

(In the following problems use 450 lb. per cu. ft. as density of cast iron and 490 lb. per cu. ft. as density of steel.)

1. Compute the moment of inertia and radius of gyration of a cast-iron cylinder 2 ft. in diameter and 1 ft. long with respect to its geometric axis.

Ans. 22; 0.707 ft.

2. Compute the moment of inertia and radius of gyration of a steel sphere 6 in. in diameter with respect to its geometric axis.   *Ans.* 0.0249; 0.158 ft.

3. Compute the moment of inertia and radius of gyration of a steel rod 2 in. in diameter and 4 ft. long with respect to an axis through one end normal to the rod.   *Ans.* 7.08; 2.31 ft.

4. A slender rod 6 ft. long and weighing 50 lb. is mounted on an axle normal to the rod and 1 ft. from an end. Compute the moment of inertia.

Ans. 10.9.

5. Compute the moment of inertia of a cast-iron cylinder 3 ft. in diameter and weighing 100 lb. with respect to an element of its curved surface.

Ans. 10.5.

6. Determine the moment of inertia of the cylinder in Prob. 5 with respect to a diameter of the base.   *Ans.* 1.75.

Supplementary Problems

1. Compute the moment of inertia of a hollow steel cylinder 12 in. outside diameter, 6 in. inside diameter, and 2 ft. long, with respect to its geometric axis.   *Ans.* 2.8.

2. Compute the moment of inertia of the hollow cylinder described in Prob. 1 with respect to an element of the inside curved surface. *Ans.* 3.92.

3. A cast-iron governor ball 3 in. in diameter is attached to a steel rod 9 in. long and 1 in. in diameter. The system rotates about a vertical axis at an angle of 30° with the rod. Compute the moment of inertia with respect to the axis of rotation.   *Ans.* 0.0255.

4. A sector of 60°, cut out of a circular disk, is shown in Fig. 248. The weight of the sector is 30 lb. Compute its moment of inertia with respect to an axis through O perpendicular to the plane of the figure.   *Ans.* 0.207.

5. Determine, by the method of the example of Art. 53, the moment of inertia of a right circular cone with respect to an axis through the vertex parallel to the base.

$$Ans. \ \tfrac{3}{5} M(\tfrac{1}{4}r^2 + h^2).$$

6. From the result of Prob. 5, determine, without further integration, the moment of inertia of the cone with respect to a diameter of the base. $Ans. \ \tfrac{3}{10}M(\tfrac{1}{2}r^2 + \tfrac{1}{3}h^2).$

Fig. 248.

7. The bases of a conical steel frustum of 8-in. altitude are 12 in. and 6 in. in diameter. A concentric hole of 4-in. diameter extends from base to base. Compute the moment of inertia of the hollow frustum with respect to its geometric axis.   *Ans.* 0.373.

8. A hemispherical cast-iron bowl of 12-in. outside radius and 10-in. inside radius rotates about its geometric axis. Compute the moment of inertia.

Ans. **7.0.**

Fig. 249.

9. A cast-iron flywheel with solid web has dimensions as shown in Fig. 249. Compute its moment of inertia with respect to the axis of rotation.

Ans. **20.6.**

. Fig. 250.

10. Determine by integration the moment of inertia of the torus, Fig. 250, with respect to the x axis. *Ans.* $I = M(\frac{3}{4}r^2 + R^2)$.

PART II—KINETICS

CHAPTER VIII

RECTILINEAR MOTION

Art. 55. Fundamental and Derived Quantities; Dimensional Equations. A physical quantity which cannot be defined in terms of other physical quantities is called a *fundamental* quantity. In mechanics, time, space, and either force or mass are the fundamental quantities. A system of units based on time, space, and mass as fundamental quantities is known as an *absolute* system; one based on time, space, and force as fundamental is known as a *gravitational* system. In either system, any quantity not fundamental may be defined in terms of the fundamental quantities and is known as a *derived* quantity.

The dimensions of a physical quantity are determined by the fundamental quantities involved and the degree to which they occur. Thus velocity, which is expressed as distance per unit of time, as shown later, has the dimensions L/T or LT^{-1}, where L denotes length, and T denotes time. Moment of inertia of area has the dimensions L^4. Moment of inertia of mass has dimensions ML^2 when the absolute system is used. If each term of an equation involving physical quantities is replaced by its dimensions, the resulting equation is called a dimensional equation. Any algebraic equation involving physical quantities must be homogeneous; that is, each term must be of the same dimensions. This principle is of value in checking the correctness of equations and also in determining the units in which a result is expressed.

In subsequent articles, the dimensions of each unit as defined or derived will be given in terms of mass, length, and time (M, L, T). The symbol $\approx$ will be used to denote dimensional equality. Thus,

$$I = Mk^2 \approx ML^2$$

142

Art. 56. Displacement. The motion of a body is *rectilinear* when it is confined to a straight-line path. The distance of the moving body from a given point of reference in the path is called the *displacement*. Displacement may be measured in any units of length, the foot being the most common unit in kinetics.

Displacement is a vector quantity, having direction as well as magnitude, and may be represented graphically by a vector. Thus, displacements may be combined to obtain a resultant displacement, or may be resolved into components.

Art. 57. Velocity. *Velocity* is the time rate of change of displacement. If velocity is represented by v, displacement by s, and time by t, then

$$\mathbf{v} = \frac{ds}{dt}$$

When velocity is constant, the above relation becomes

$$v = \frac{s}{t} \approx LT^{-1}$$

Velocity may be expressed in terms of any units of length and time, feet per second and miles per hour being the more common units.

Velocity, being a vector quantity, may be represented graphically by a vector. In common with other vector quantities, velocities may be combined into a resultant or resolved into components. *Speed* is a scalar quantity, representing only the magnitude of a velocity without involving any particular sense of direction.

Problems

1. A car has a velocity of 30 mi. per hr. What is its velocity in feet per second? *Ans.* 44 ft. per sec.

2. The displacement of a ball thrown vertically upward with initial velocity of 50 ft. per sec. is given by the equation $s = 50\,t - 16.1\,t^2$, where s is in feet and t is in seconds. Derive the equation for the velocity, and determine the velocity at the end of 2 seconds.
Ans. $v = 50 - 32.2\,t$; 14.4 ft. per sec. downward.

3. If the motion of a body is described by the equation $s = \frac{1}{2}\sin 2\pi t$, determine the velocity at the end of (a) 1 sec.; (b) 2.25 sec.
Ans. 3.14 ft. per sec.; zero.

4. A bullet traveling with a constant velocity of 1000 ft. per sec. strikes a target. The sound of striking returns to the point of firing in 0.8 sec. after firing. If the velocity of sound is 1120 ft. per sec., how far away was the target? *Ans.* 423 ft.

Art. 58. Acceleration. *Acceleration* is the time rate of change of velocity. If acceleration is denoted by a, then

$$a = \frac{dv}{dt} = \frac{d^2s}{dt^2} \approx LT^{-2}$$

If the acceleration is constant, the above relation becomes

$$a = \frac{v - v_0}{t}$$

where v = final velocity, and v_0 = initial velocity. Acceleration may be expressed in terms of any units of velocity and time. The unit most commonly employed in kinetics is the foot per second per second, written *ft. per sec. per sec.* or *ft. per sec.*^{2}.

If dt is eliminated from the equations $v = ds/dt$ and $a = dv/dt$, the resulting relation is

$$v\,dv = a\,ds$$

This equation is of particular importance in problems involving variable acceleration. When the acceleration a is expressed in terms of displacement s, the above equation can be integrated.

Acceleration has direction as well as magnitude and is therefore a vector quantity. Like other vector quantities, accelerations may be represented graphically by vectors, and may be combined or resolved.

Problems

1. An automobile attains a velocity of 30 mi. per hr. from a standing start in 8 sec. Determine its average acceleration in feet per second per second.
Ans. 5.5 ft. per sec. per sec.

2. A train decreases its speed from 40 mi. per hr. to 25 mi. per hr. in 10 sec. Compute the average acceleration. *Ans.* −2.2 ft. per sec. per sec.

3. For the motion described in Prob. 3, Art. 57, determine the acceleration at the end of (*a*) 1 sec.; (*b*) 2.25 sec.
Ans. zero; 19.75 ft. per sec. per sec.

4. The acceleration of a moving body is $a = 0.4s$. If the initial velocity was 2 ft. per sec., determine the velocity after moving 5 ft. (Note that the acceleration is variable.) *Ans.* 3.74 ft. per sec.

Art. 59. Uniformly Accelerated Motion. If a body has constant acceleration, the average velocity may be expressed as

$$v_{\text{av.}} = \tfrac{1}{2}\,(v + v_0)$$

and its displacement may be expressed as

$$s = v_{av.} \times t = \tfrac{1}{2}(v + v_0)t \tag{1}$$

Also, from Art. 58,

$$a = \frac{v - v_0}{t} \quad \text{or} \quad v = v_0 + at \tag{2}$$

If v is eliminated from equations (1) and (2) the following relation is obtained

$$s = v_0 t + \tfrac{1}{2}at^2 \tag{3}$$

If t is eliminated from equations (1) and (2) the following relation is obtained

$$v^2 = v_0{}^2 + 2as \tag{4}$$

Equations (1) to (4) are known as the equations of uniformly accelerated rectilinear motion. By their use, any problem involving this type of motion may be solved. These equations may also be obtained by means of the calculus from the definitions of velocity and acceleration, $v = ds/dt$ and $a = dv/dt$.

Example

Two cars, A and B, accelerate from a standing start. The acceleration of A is 4 ft. per sec.[2], and that of B is 5 ft. per sec.[2] If B was orignally 20 ft. behind A, how long will it take B to overtake A?

Solution: Let t represent the time for each car, and x the distance traveled by A. Then the distance traveled by B will be $x + 20$. Writing the equation

$$s = v_0 t + \tfrac{1}{2}at^2$$

for each car, the resulting equations are:

For A $\qquad\qquad\qquad x = 0 + \tfrac{1}{2}(4)t^2$

For B $\qquad\qquad\qquad x + 20 = 0 + \tfrac{1}{2}(5)t^2$

Simultaneous solution of these equations gives

$$x = 80 \text{ ft. and } t = 6.32 \text{ sec.}$$

Problems

1. Derive equations (2), (3), and (4) of this article by calculus, starting with the definitions of velocity and acceleration, $v = ds/dt$ and $a = dv/dt$.

2. An automobile is brought to rest from a velocity of 45 mi. per hr. in a distance of 200 ft. Determine the average acceleration and the time to come to rest. *Ans.* −10.9 ft. per sec. per sec.; 6.06 sec.

3. A car with initial velocity of 15 mi. per hr. is accelerated at the rate of 2 ft. per sec. per sec. Determine the velocity acquired and the distance traveled in 5 sec. *Ans.* 32 ft. per sec.; 135 ft.

4. Two elevators in adjacent shafts approach each other, one from the top, the other from the bottom. Each starts at the same instant from rest 400 ft. apart. The top car has downward acceleration of 2 ft. per sec. per sec. The other has upward acceleration of 1 ft. per sec. per sec. When and where do they pass? *Ans.* 16.3 sec.; 133 ft. from the bottom.

5. Solve Prob. 4, if the lower car starts 2 sec. after the upper one.
Ans. 17 sec.; 112 ft. from bottom.

Art. 60. Motion of a Freely Falling Body.

The attraction exerted by the earth on material bodies varies, being dependent on latitude and elevation above sea-level. Since, as will be shown later, acceleration is proportional to force, the acceleration of gravity varies from place to place. This variation is so slight that, for relatively small distances from the earth's surface, it may be neglected in treating the motion of falling bodies, and the acceleration of gravity may be considered as constant. If the acceleration of gravity is represented by g and vertical displacement by h, the equations of Art. 59 become:

$$\mathbf{h} = \tfrac{1}{2}(\mathbf{v} + \mathbf{v}_0)\mathbf{t} \tag{1}$$

$$\mathbf{v} = \mathbf{v}_0 + \mathbf{g}\mathbf{t} \tag{2}$$

$$\mathbf{h} = \mathbf{v}_0\mathbf{t} + \tfrac{1}{2}\mathbf{g}\mathbf{t}^2 \tag{3}$$

$$\mathbf{v}^2 = \mathbf{v}_0{}^2 + 2\mathbf{g}\mathbf{h} \tag{4}$$

These are known as the equations of a freely falling body. In this book the value of g will be taken as 32.2 ft. per sec. per sec.

Example

A ball is dropped from rest at the top of a tower 200 ft. high. Two seconds later a second ball is thrown vertically upward from the ground with initial velocity of 100 ft. per sec. At what distance above the ground will they pass?

Solution: Let y represent the distance above the ground where the balls meet, t the time for the first ball, and $t - 2$ the time for the second. The equation of motion to be used is

$$h = v_0 t + \tfrac{1}{2}g t^2$$

Taking downward as the positive direction for the first ball, the equation becomes

$$200 - y = 0 + \tfrac{1}{2}(+32.2)t^2 \tag{1}$$

Taking upward as the positive direction for the second ball, the equation becomes

$$y = (+100)(t - 2) + \tfrac{1}{2}(-32.2)(t - 2)^2 \tag{2}$$

Simultaneous solution of equations (1) and (2) gives

$$t = 2.82 \text{ sec. and } y = 72 \text{ ft.}$$

Problems

1. Solve the example above if the two balls start at the same instant.

Ans. 2 sec.; 136 ft.

2. A body is projected vertically upward with an initial velocity of 200 ft. per sec. To what height will it rise? In what time will it return to the starting position? Determine the velocity and distance above the ground 4 sec. after it starts.

Ans. 621 ft.; 12.4 sec.; 71.2 ft. per sec. upward; 542 ft.

3. From the top of a building 150 ft. high a ball is thrown vertically upward with an initial velocity of 20 ft. per sec. How long will it take to strike the ground below? With what velocity will it strike?

Ans. 3.74 sec.; 100 ft. per sec.

4. A ball is projected vertically upward with an initial velocity of 60 ft. per sec. One second later, a second ball is projected vertically upward with the same initial velocity. Where and when do they pass?

Ans. 2.36 sec.; 51.6 ft.

5. A stone is dropped from a bridge into the water below. If sound has velocity of 1120 ft. per sec. and the sound of the splash is heard on the bridge 3.5 sec. after the stone was released, determine the elevation of the bridge above the water.

Ans. 180 ft.

Art. 61. Force, Mass, and Acceleration. According to Newton's second law of motion, a body subjected to the action of an unbalanced force will experience an acceleration proportional to the force and inversely proportional to the mass of the body. This relation is expressed by the equation

$$\mathbf{a} = \frac{\mathbf{F}}{\mathbf{M}} \quad \text{or} \quad \mathbf{F} = \mathbf{Ma} \approx MLT^{-2}$$

In order that F and a in the above equation may be expressed in the customary engineering units, pounds and feet per second per second respectively, it is necessary to express the mass M in terms of a unit called the *slug*, which consists of g pounds. To avoid a possible confusion of units, it is convenient to eliminate M from the above equation.   If the force acting on a body is its own weight W, then the resulting acceleration will be that of gravity g.   Hence

$$W = Mg$$

If this equation is divided into the preceding one, the result is

$$\frac{F}{W} = \frac{a}{g} \quad \text{or} \quad \mathbf{F} = \frac{\mathbf{W}\mathbf{a}}{\mathbf{g}}$$

Thus, M is replaced by W/g, and the customary engineering units may be used for all quantities involved.

It should be particularly noted that the force F represents the unbalanced or resultant force acting on a body.   It is often called the *effective* force since it is that force which is effective in producing acceleration.   Since the effective force for a body is the resultant of all the effective forces acting on the individual particles of mass composing the body, it must act through the center of gravity of the body.

Example

A 50-lb. horizontal force is applied to a 60-lb. block, Fig. 251, on a 30° incline for which the coefficient of friction is 0.1. Determine the resulting acceleration of the block.

FIG. 251.

Solution: By summation of forces in the direction normal to the plane

$$N = 60 \cos 30° + 50 \sin 30° = 77 \text{ lb.}$$

then

$$F_1 = fN = 0.1 \times 77 = 7.7 \text{ lb.}$$

The unbalanced or effective force parallel to the direction of motion is then

$$F = 50 \cos 30° - 7.7 - 60 \sin 30° = 5.6 \text{ lb.}$$

The resulting acceleration is thus

$$a = \frac{Fg}{W} = \frac{5.6 \times 32.2}{60} = 3 \text{ ft. per sec.}^2$$

Problems

1. A block starts from rest and slides down a 30° incline. Compute the velocity at the end of 20 ft.: (a) if the surface is smooth; (b) if the coefficient of friction is 0.2.   *Ans.* 25.4 ft. per sec.; 20.5 ft. per sec.

2. A 2-ton elevator, descending with velocity of 10 ft. per sec., is brought to rest in a distance of 20 ft. Determine the tension in the supporting cables while the elevator comes to rest.   *Ans.* 4310 lb.

3. A train of 50 cars each weighing 40 tons is hauled up a $\frac{1}{2}$ per cent grade. Train resistance is 8 lb. per ton. Determine the drawbar pull required to change the velocity of the train from 10 mi. per hr. to 25 mi. per hr. in a distance of $\frac{1}{2}$ mile.   *Ans.* 31.2 tons.

4. While a car is brought to rest from a speed of 30 mi. per hr. in a distance of 80 ft. a block resting on the floor of the car is on the point of slipping. Determine the coefficient of friction.

Ans. 0.376.

Fig. 252.

5. If the coefficient of friction is 0.4 for the 150 lb. block shown in Fig. 252, determine the acceleration of the system and the cable tension.   *Ans.* 2.15 ft. per sec. per sec.; 70 lb.

Art. 62. Reversed Effective Force; D'Alembert's Principle.

Since an acceleration can be produced only by an unbalanced force, it is obvious that the system of forces acting on a body having acceleration is not in equilibrium, and the conditions of static equilibrium $\Sigma F_x = 0$, $\Sigma F_y = 0$, and $\Sigma M = 0$ cannot be applied to the system of actual forces. *However, if a force equal to the effective force Wa/g, but opposite in direction and collinear, were added to the actual force system, the resulting system would then be in equilibrium and the equations of static equilibrium would then apply.* It thus results that, although the forces acting on a body possessing acceleration are not in equilibrium, static conditions may be produced by the addition of an imaginary force Wa/g acting through the center of gravity of the body and parallel but *opposite in direction to the acceleration.* This statement is known as D'Alembert's principle, and the added force is called the *reversed effective* force, the D'Alembert force, or the inertia force. The use of this principle is of considerable advantage in the solution of many problems involving force and acceleration.

Example 1

A 4000-lb. car is brought to rest from a speed of 30 mi. per hr. in a distance of 60 ft. by means of brakes. The center of gravity of the car is 2.5 ft. above the ground and midway between front and rear wheels which are 10 ft. apart, center to center. Determine the normal pressure acting on the front wheels as the car is brought to rest.

Solution: The acceleration of the car is first determined:

$$a = \frac{v^2 - v_o{}^2}{2s} = \frac{0 - (44)^2}{2 \times 60} = -16.1 \text{ ft. per sec.}^2$$

The reversed effective force is then

$$\frac{Wa}{g} = \frac{4000 \times 16.1}{32.2} = 2000 \text{ lb.}$$

The free-body diagram of the car is shown in Fig. 253 with the addition of the reversed effective force acting through the center of gravity, and opposite in direction to the acceleration. The forces F_1 and F_2 represent

Fig. 253.

the frictional forces induced by brake action on front and rear wheels respectively.

Since static conditions now prevail, the required normal pressure N_1 on the front wheels may be obtained by moments about B:

$$\Sigma M_B = 10N_1 - 4000 \times 5 - 2000 \times 2\tfrac{1}{2} = 0$$

from which

$$N_1 = 2500 \text{ lb.}$$

showing that an additional pressure of 500 lb. over static conditions is produced on the front wheels in stopping the car, together with a corresponding reduction in pressure on the rear wheels.

Example 2

A 600-lb. block on a 30° incline is connected to a 150-lb. block hanging vertically by a cable running over a pulley as shown in Fig. 254 (a). The coefficient of friction between block and incline is 0.2. Neglecting the mass of the pulley and its axle friction, determine the acceleration of the system, the cable tension, and the velocity after the block has moved 20 ft. from rest.

Solution: It is seen by inspection that the only possible direction of acceleration for the 600-lb. block is down the incline. The free-body

(a)   (b)   (c)

FIG. 254.

diagrams for the two blocks including the addition of the reversed effective forces are shown in Figs. 254 (b) and 254 (c).

In Fig. 254 (b)

$$\Sigma F_y = N - 600 \cos 30° = 0$$

$$N = 520 \text{ lb.,} \quad \text{and therefore} \quad F = 0.2N = 104 \text{ lb.}$$

$$\Sigma F_x = T + \frac{600a}{32.2} + 104 - 600 \sin 30° = 0 \tag{1}$$

In Fig. 254 (c)

$$\Sigma F_v = T - \frac{150a}{32.2} - 150 = 0 \tag{2}$$

By simultaneous solution of (1) and (2)

$$T = 159 \text{ lb.} \quad \text{and} \quad a = 1.98 \text{ ft. per sec.}^2$$

Finally

$$v^2 = v_o^2 + 2as = 0 + 2 \times 1.98 \times 20$$

$$v = 8.9 \text{ ft. per sec.}$$

Problems

1. A rectangular block 2 ft. square and 5 ft. long stands on end on the floor of a car with its sides parallel to those of the car. If friction is sufficient to prevent sliding, what acceleration may the car have before the block tips? *Ans.* 12.9 ft. per sec. per sec.

2. Assume that the car in Ex. 1 above has brakes applied to the rear wheels only and that the maximum resistance that can be developed due to friction between wheel and road is one-half the corresponding normal pressure. Determine the distance in which the car can be brought to rest from the velocity of 30 mi. per hr., and the normal reaction at front wheels while the car is coming to rest. *Ans.* 135 ft.; 2220 lb.

3. If the coefficient of friction on the incline, Fig. 255, is 0.25, determine the weight W required to give the 200-lb. body an upward acceleration of 2.5 ft. per sec. per sec. Compute the cable tension. *Ans.* 835 lb.; 108 lb.

Fig. 255. Fig. 256.

4. A door is hung on a track as shown in Fig. 256. The door weighs 400 lb. with its center of gravity at C. The coefficient of friction for each of the shoes A and B and the track is 1/5. If the force P applied to the door is 200 lb., determine the resulting acceleration and the normal pressures at A and B. *Ans.* 9.66 ft. per sec. per sec.; 275 lb.; 125 lb.

5. Solve Prob. 4 if the shoe at A is replaced by a wheel which rolls freely without resistance. *Ans.* 13.6 ft. per sec. per sec.; 244 lb.; 156 lb.

Supplementary Problems

1. A mine cage is rising with uniform velocity of 10 ft. per sec. When it is 200 ft. below the surface a rock is released from rest at the top of the shaft. At what distance from the surface does the rock strike the cage? *Ans.* 168 ft.

2. Solve Prob. 1 if the cage is descending with the same velocity. *Ans.* 239 ft.

3. Two cars A and B have velocity of 60 mi. per hr. in the same direction. Car A is 250 ft. behind car B when brakes are applied to B, causing it to decelerate at the rate of 10 ft. per sec. per sec. In what time will A overtake B, and how far will each have traveled? *Ans.* 7.07 sec.; 622 ft.; 372 ft.

4. A freight car with velocity of 6 mi. per hr. is switched to a 1 per cent up-grade. If car resistance is 4 lb. per ton, how far up the grade will the car go? *Ans.* 100 ft.

5. The two weights shown in Fig. 257 are released from rest. Neglecting mass of pulley and cord, compute the tension T in the cable supporting the pulley. *Ans.* 114 lb.

FIG. 257.

FIG. 258.

6. If the weights shown in Fig. 258 are released from rest, determine the acceleration of each and the cable tension.

Ans. $a_{20} = 5.85$ ft. per sec. per sec.; $T = 16.4$ lb.

7. The velocity of a block sliding down a 45° incline increases from 10 ft. per sec. to 25 ft. per sec. in a distance of 15 ft. down the incline. Compute the coefficient of friction. *Ans.* 0.23.

8. A car weighing 2000 lb. is pulled by a horizontal force of 400 lb. applied 2 ft. above the track. The center of gravity of the car is 3 ft. above the track and midway between front and rear wheels which are 8 ft. apart, center to center. Frictional resistance acting at the track on each set of wheels is one-tenth the corresponding normal pressure. Compute the acceleration of the car and the normal pressure on the front wheels.

Ans. 3.22 ft. per sec. per sec.; 1025 lb.

9. If the coefficient of friction under the 300-lb. block in Fig. 259 is 0.1, determine its acceleration and the cable tension.

Ans. 1.55 ft. per sec. per sec. up the incline; 190 lb.

FIG. 259.

FIG. 260.

10. Solve Prob. 9 if the blocks are connected with a pulley and cable arrangement as shown in Fig. 260.

Ans. 2.21 ft. per sec. per sec. down the incline; 103 lb.

11. The center of gravity of a 4000-lb. car is 2.5 ft. above the ground and midway between front and rear wheels which are 10 ft. apart center to center.

While the car is traveling at 45 mi. per hr., brakes are set on the rear wheels inducing resistance at the pavement equal to the normal pressure on these wheels. Compute the distance in which the car will come to rest.

Ans. 169 ft.

12. A train of 20 cars weighing 50 tons each reaches a $\frac{1}{2}$ per cent up-grade 2 miles long with a velocity of 30 mi. per hr. If the drawbar pull is 12,000 lb. and train resistance is 6 lb. per ton, with what velocity will the train reach the top of the grade? *Ans.* 16.4 mi. per hr.

FIG. 261.

13. If the train of Prob. 12 travels on level track after reaching the top of the grade and the drawbar pull remains unchanged, in what distance will it regain its original velocity of 30 mi. per hr.? *Ans.* 1.33 mi.

14. The system of weights in Fig. 261 is released from rest. Neglecting mass of cords and pulleys, determine the tension T, supporting the system, and the velocity of each weight 1 sec. later.

Ans. $T = 16.9$ lb.; $v_3 = 13.3$ ft. per sec. upward; $v_6 = 9.49$ ft. per sec. downward; $v_9 = 1.90$ ft. per sec. downward.

15. Two freight cars A and B, coupled together with B behind A, are coasting down a 2 per cent grade. Car A weighs 20 tons and B weighs 30 tons. Train resistance is 8 lb. per ton. When the velocity of the cars is 30 mi. per hr., brakes are set on car A inducing an additional resistance of 200 lb. per ton. Determine the distance the cars move in coming to rest and the compression in the coupler.

Ans. 1250 ft.; 2400 lb.

CHAPTER IX

CURVILINEAR MOTION AND ROTATION

Art. 63. Velocity and Acceleration in Curvilinear Motion. If a particle moves in a curved path, its motion is said to be *curvilinear*. Only plane curvilinear motion will be discussed in this book.

The velocity of a body moving along a curved path changes in direction from point to point and may also change in magnitude. At any given point the velocity is in the direction of the tangent to the curve at that point. In Fig. 262 (*a*), *ABCD* represents a

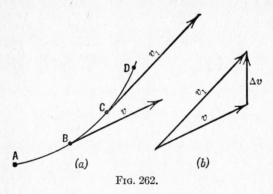

Fig. 262.

curved path; *B* and *C* are any two points in the path at which the velocities of the moving particle are *v* and v_1 respectively, tangent to the curve at these points. The change in velocity that has taken place in going from *B* to *C* is shown by the vector Δv in Fig. 262 (*b*).

Since the velocity in curvilinear motion necessarily changes in direction and may also change in magnitude, it follows that there is always acceleration. If the time required to travel from *B* to *C* in Fig. 262 (*a*) is denoted by Δt, then the ratio of the total change of velocity Δv to the time Δt gives the average acceleration between

155

B and *C*.   The limiting value of the ratio $\Delta v/\Delta t$ as Δt approaches zero becomes the instantaneous value of the acceleration.

Art. 64. Normal and Tangential Components of Acceleration.
It is evident from the preceding discussion that the direction of the acceleration is usually not in the direction of the velocity of the particle.   For convenience, the total acceleration will be resolved into two components, a_t and a_n.   The component a_t, taken in the direction of the velocity, is tangent to the path of travel and is called the *tangential acceleration*.   The component a_n, taken in a direction perpendicular to the velocity, is called the *normal acceleration*.

In Fig. 263 (*a*), *B* and *C* are consecutive points in the path at a differential distance *ds* apart.   The time from *B* to *C*, also differ-

Fig. 263.

ential, is denoted by *dt*.   The total change in velocity is the vector $FE = \Delta v$, shown in Fig. 263 (*b*).   The total acceleration is the limiting value of the ratio $\Delta v/\Delta t$ as Δt approaches zero.

In Fig. 263 (*b*), the velocity change Δv is resolved into its tangential component *GE*, parallel to the velocity at *C*, and its normal component *GF*, normal to the velocity at *C*.   The tangential acceleration is then

$$a_t = \frac{GE}{dt} = \frac{v_1 - v \cos d\theta}{dt}$$

The limiting value of $\cos d\theta$, as $d\theta$ approaches zero, is unity.   Also, as $d\theta$ approaches zero, the difference $v_1 - v$ becomes dv.   Hence,

$$a_t = \frac{dv}{dt}$$

The tangential acceleration is thus the time rate of change of the magnitude of the velocity. If the velocity of a particle having curvilinear motion is constant in magnitude, the tangential acceleration will be zero.

From Fig. 263 (b), the normal acceleration is

$$a_n = \frac{GF}{dt} = \frac{v \sin d\theta}{dt} = \frac{v \, d\theta}{dt}$$

From Fig. 263 (a) $d\theta = ds/\rho$. Also, by definition, $ds/dt = v$. Therefore

$$\mathbf{a_n} = \frac{v \, d\theta}{dt} = \frac{v \, ds}{\rho \, dt} = \frac{\mathbf{v}^2}{\boldsymbol{\rho}}$$

If the radius of curvature is constant, the normal acceleration may be written

$$\mathbf{a_n} = \frac{\mathbf{v}^2}{\mathbf{r}}$$

It is apparent from the above results that there will always be normal acceleration as long as the direction of velocity changes and that its direction is towards the center of curvature.

It has previously been shown (Art. 61) that the effective force acting on a body moving with acceleration is $Ma = \dfrac{Wa}{g}$. For a body having curvilinear motion there must be a tangential effective force

$$\mathbf{F_t} = \frac{W}{g} a_t = \frac{\mathbf{W}}{\mathbf{g}} \frac{\mathbf{dv}}{\mathbf{dt}}$$

and a normal effective force

$$\mathbf{F_n} = \frac{W}{g} a_n = \frac{\mathbf{W}}{\mathbf{g}} \frac{\mathbf{v}^2}{\boldsymbol{\rho}}$$

In the solution of problems involving forces acting on a body moving with curvilinear motion, the D'Alembert principle (Art. 62) may be used. This consists of adding the effective forces, reversed in direction, to the free body and then applying the conditions of static equilibrium. The normal reversed effective force, directed away from the center of curvature, is commonly called *centrifugal* force.

Art. 65. Conical Pendulum. The conical pendulum consists of a small body suspended by a cord from a support and rotating about a vertical axis through the support, as shown in Fig. 264 (*a*). The free body is acted upon by the tension T in the cord and its weight W.   To these is added the normal reversed effective force Wv^2/gr, directed away from the center, as shown in Fig. 264 (*b*). If the speed of rotation is constant, the tangential acceleration and the tangential reversed effective force are zero.   If the speed of rotation is variable, the tangential reversed effective force to be

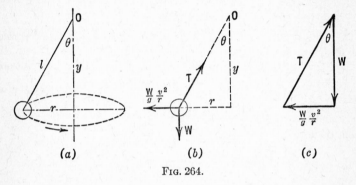

(*a*)   (*b*)   (*c*)

Fig. 264.

added is normal to the plane of the forces shown and so does not affect the solution.

From the triangle of forces, Fig. 264 (*c*),

$$\tan \theta = \frac{Wv^2/gr}{W} = \frac{v^2}{gr}$$

The velocity v is obtained by writing the equation of moments with respect to point O,

$$Wr = \frac{Wv^2}{gr} \cdot y$$

$$v = r\sqrt{\frac{g}{y}}$$

The time t for one complete revolution about the axis is

$$t = \frac{s}{v} = \frac{2\pi r}{r\sqrt{\dfrac{g}{y}}} = 2\pi\sqrt{\frac{y}{g}}$$

The number of revolutions per second is

$$n = \frac{1}{t} = \frac{1}{2\pi}\sqrt{\frac{g}{y}}$$

From the above relation, $y = g/4\pi^2 n^2$, showing that the height y of the conical pendulum is independent of its length l and depends only on its speed of rotation.

Example

A 10-lb. weight at the end of a 20-in. cord is rotated about a vertical axis at such speed that it makes an angle of 30° with the axis. Determine the linear velocity, the tension in the cord, and the time for 1 revolution.

Solution: From the triangle of forces, Fig. 264 (c),

$$T = W/\cos\theta = 10/\cos 30° = 11.5 \text{ lb.}$$

From the relation $v = r\sqrt{\dfrac{g}{y}}$,

$$v = \tfrac{20}{12}\sin 30° \sqrt{\frac{32.2}{\tfrac{20}{12}\cos 30°}} = 3.93 \text{ ft. per sec.}$$

From the relation $t = 2\pi\sqrt{\dfrac{y}{g}}$,

$$t = 2\pi\sqrt{\frac{\tfrac{20}{12}\cos 30°}{32.2}} = 1.33 \text{ sec.}$$

Problems

1. A conical pendulum of 2-ft. length rotates at 60° with its vertical axis. Compute the linear velocity.   *Ans.* 9.83 ft. per sec.

2. If the conical pendulum of Prob. 1 has a linear velocity of 6.5 ft. per sec., determine the angle from the vertical at which it rotates. *Ans.* 43.5°.

Art. 66. Superelevation of Curved Roadways and Tracks.

It is a matter of common experience that a vehicle traveling around a curve tends to skid toward the outside of the curve and to overturn. The relations between the forces acting will now be considered. In Fig. 265 is shown the free-body diagram of a car rounding a curve whose surface is horizontal and whose center is to the left. The forces consist of the weight W of the car, the normal pressures N_1 and N_2 on inner and outer wheels, the corresponding frictional forces F_1 and F_2 tending to prevent skidding outward, and the normal reversed effective force Wv^2/gr acting horizontally through the center of gravity C. If F represents the resultant of F_1 and F_2, N the resultant of N_1 and N_2, and f the coefficient of friction, then

$$F = F_1 + F_2 \quad \text{and} \quad N = N_1 + N_2 = W$$

$$F = fN = fW$$

By summation of forces horizontally,

$$Wv^2/gr - fW = 0$$

$$v^2 = fgr \quad \text{and} \quad v = \sqrt{fgr}$$

The above equation gives the maximum velocity with which the car may round the curve without skidding.

FIG. 265.

If the friction is sufficient to prevent skidding it is still possible for the car to overturn. In Fig. 265, N_1 and F_1 are zero when tipping of the car impends. The equation of moments with respect to point A then gives

$$W \cdot \frac{d}{2} - \frac{Wv^2}{gr} \cdot y = 0$$

$$v = \sqrt{\frac{dgr}{2y}}$$

The above equation gives the maximum velocity with which the car can round the curve without overturning.

A higher velocity in either of the above cases is made possible by superelevating or banking the curve. This consists of sloping the surface so that the outer edge of the curve is above the level of the inner edge. In Fig. 266 (a), θ is the angle of superelevation required so that there will be zero side thrust on the wheels of the car for the velocity v. From the triangle of forces, Fig. 266 (b),

$$\tan \theta = \frac{v^2}{gr}$$

At velocities lower than v, the car tends to slide down the slope and a side thrust on the wheels results in the direction toward the

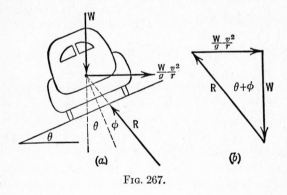

Fig. 266.

outside. At velocities higher than v, the car tends to slide outward and a side thrust results in a direction toward the inside.

The maximum velocity with which the car can round the banked curve without skidding will now be determined. In Fig.

Fig. 267.

267 (a), the resultant of the normal and frictional forces is represented by R, inclined to the normal at the limiting angle of static friction $\phi = \tan^{-1}f$. From the force triangle, shown in Fig. 267 (b),

$$\tan (\theta + \phi) = \frac{v^2}{gr}$$

The preceding method of analysis may also be applied to the superelevation of railroad curves. In this case the side thrust is the pressure exerted by the rails on the flanges of the wheels.

Example 1

Determine the angle of superelevation for a highway curve of 600-ft. radius so that there will be no side thrust for a speed of 45 mi. per hr. At what speed will skidding impend if the coefficient of friction is 0.3?

Solution: For zero side thrust,

$$\theta = \tan^{-1}\frac{v^2}{gr} = \tan^{-1}\frac{(66)^2}{32.2 \times 600} = 12.7°$$

The angle of friction is

$$\phi = \tan^{-1} 0.3 = 16.7°$$

When skidding impends, $\tan(\theta + \phi) = \dfrac{v^2}{gr}$

$$\tan(12.7° + 16.7°) = \frac{v^2}{32.2 \times 600}$$

$$v = 104 \text{ ft. per sec.} = 71.2 \text{ mi. per hr.}$$

Example 2

Determine the superelevation of the outer rail of a track of 4.9-ft. gage (distance center to center of rails) on a curve of 3000-ft. radius so that there will be no flange pressure at a speed of 30 mi. per hr. If a 60,000-lb. car has a velocity of 45 mi. per hr. on the curve, what is the flange pressure?

Solution: The tangent of the required angle of superelevation is

$$\tan \theta = \frac{v^2}{gr} = \frac{(44)^2}{32.2 \times 3000} = 0.02$$

The amount of superelevation of the outer rail is

$$e = 4.9 \sin \theta = 4.9 \times 0.02 = 0.098 \text{ ft.} = 1.18 \text{ in.}$$

From the free-body diagram, Fig. 268,

$$\Sigma F_x = P + W \sin \theta - \frac{Wv^2}{gr} \cos \theta = 0$$

Since angle θ is very small, $\sin \theta = \tan \theta = 0.02$ and $\cos \theta = 1$. The above equation then becomes

$$P + 60{,}000 \times 0.02 - \frac{60{,}000 \times (66)^2}{32.2 \times 3000} \times 1 = 0$$

$$P = 1500 \text{ lb.}$$

FIG. 268.

Problems

1. Determine the maximum speed at which a car may round a curve of 500-ft. radius without skidding if the coefficient of friction is 0.8 and the curve is not superelevated.   *Ans.* 77.5 mi. per hr.

2. If the tread of the car in Prob. 1 is 60 in. and the center of gravity is 28 in. above the road, determine the velocity at which tipping would impend.
Ans. 89.5 mi. per hr.

3. If a curve of 600-ft. radius is banked for zero side thrust at 60 mi. per hr., what is the side thrust on the wheels of a 3000-lb. car with velocity of 80 mi. per hr.?   *Ans.* 860 lb.

4. If the coefficient of friction is 0.5, at what speed would skidding impend for the car in Prob. 3?   *Ans.* 100 mi. per hr.

5. Compute the superelevation of the outer rail of a railroad track of 2000-ft. radius for zero flange pressure for a velocity of 45 mi. per hr. The distance between rails is 4.9 ft.   *Ans.* 3.97 in.

6. Compute the flange pressure on the wheels of a 60-ton car with velocity of 45 mi. per hr. on a 4° curve superelevated for velocity of 30 mi. per hr. (a 4° curve is one in which a chord 100 ft. long subtends an angle of 4° at the center.)   *Ans.* 6300 lb.

7. Solve Prob. 6 if the velocity of the car is 15 mi. per hr.   *Ans.* −3780 lb.

Art. 67. Simple Pendulum. An ideal simple pendulum consists of a particle suspended by a weightless cord and vibrating in a vertical arc under the influence of gravity and the tension in the supporting cord. These ideal conditions are closely approximated by suspending a small heavy body at the end of a light cord. Such an arrangement is shown in Fig. 269 (*a*), in which *B* represents any position in the arc of travel ACD. The free-body diagram of the body in this position is shown in Fig. 269 (b). The system of forces consists of the weight of the body and the cord tension to which have been added the tangential and normal reversed effective forces. Since the tangential acceleration is always directed along the path toward C, the tangential reversed effective force

(a)   (b)

Fig. 269.

will be directed away from C. The tension in the cord is determined by summation of forces in the normal direction.

$$T = W \cos \theta + \frac{Wv^2}{gl} \quad [r = l]$$

By summation of forces in the tangential direction,

$$\frac{Wa_t}{g} = W \sin \theta$$

$$a_t = g \sin \theta \text{ directed toward } C$$

From Art. 58, $v\,dv = a\,ds = -g \sin \theta\,ds$. If the motion of the pendulum is restricted to small angles, $\sin \theta$ may be replaced by θ

$$v\,dv = -g\theta\,ds = -\frac{gs}{l}\,ds$$

If displacement s is measured from C and the above equation is integrated between C and B,

$$\int_{v_C}^{v} v\,dv = -\frac{g}{l}\int_{0}^{s} s\,ds$$

$$v_C^2 - v^2 = \frac{g}{l} s^2$$

When the position A is reached, $v = 0$ and $s = s_A$

$$v_C{}^2 = \frac{g}{l}\, s_A{}^2$$

By substituting this value of v_C in the preceding equation,

$$v = \sqrt{\frac{g}{l}} \cdot \sqrt{s_A{}^2 - s^2}$$

By definition,

$$v = \frac{ds}{dt}$$

$$dt = \sqrt{\frac{l}{g}} \cdot \frac{ds}{\sqrt{s_A{}^2 - s^2}}$$

If time is measured from position C, and the above equation integrated between B and C,

$$\int_0^t dt = \sqrt{\frac{l}{g}} \int_0^s \frac{ds}{\sqrt{s_A{}^2 - s^2}}$$

$$t = \sqrt{\frac{l}{g}} \, \sin^{-1} \frac{s}{s_A}$$

To determine the time from C to A, let $s = s_A$.
Then

$$t_A = \frac{\pi}{2} \sqrt{\frac{l}{g}}$$

The *period* T, or time required for a complete oscillation from A to D and back to A again, is obviously four times as great. Hence

$$\mathbf{T = 2\pi \sqrt{\frac{l}{g}}}$$

The maximum displacement from the center of the path is known as the *amplitude*. The above result shows that for small amplitudes the period of vibration is independent of the amplitude, depending only on the length of the pendulum.

Problems

1. Determine the length of a simple pendulum which will make one complete vibration in 1 sec.   *Ans.* 0.815 ft.

2. Determine the period of a simple pendulum whose length is 30 in.
                                                      Ans. 1.75 sec.

Art. 68.   Motion of a Body in a Vertical Curved Path; Friction Neglected.

In Fig. 270 (*a*) is shown a vertical frictionless curve *AB*, along which a body of weight *W* is moving under the influence of gravity and the normal reaction. The vertical distance of *A* above *B* is denoted by *h*. *C* is any position on the path at vertical distance *y* from *A*. The free-body diagram of the moving

(*a*)

(*b*)

Fig. 270.

body at *C* is shown in Fig. 270 (*b*). The normal and tangential reversed effective forces have been added. The summation of forces in the tangential direction gives

$$\frac{W a_t}{g} = W \sin \theta \quad \text{or} \quad a_t = g \sin \theta$$

$$v \, dv = a \, ds = g \sin \theta \, ds$$

Since *ds* represents a differential displacement along the curve, it may be resolved into components *dx* and *dy* as shown. Then

$$\sin \theta \cdot ds = dy$$

and,

$$v \, dv = g \, dy$$

The above differential equation is now integrated between *A* and *B*,

$$\int_{v_A}^{v_B} v \, dv = \int_0^h g \, dy$$

$$v_B{}^2 = v_A{}^2 + 2 \, \mathbf{gh}$$

This equation is identical in form to the equation (4) of a freely falling body as given in Art. 60. The change in speed of a body moving along a vertical frictionless curve is therefore the same as if it fell freely through the same vertical distance.

Example

A body of weight W is attached to a slender rod whose weight is negligible. The rod is attached at its other end to a horizontal axle. If the rod and weight are held in a vertical position above the axle, as shown in Fig. 271 (a), and then released and allowed to rotate under the influence of gravity, for what position will there be no stress in the rod?

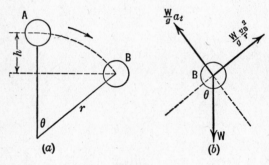

Fig. 271.

Solution: The free body diagram, including reversed effective forces, is shown in Fig. 271 (b). A summation of forces in the normal direction gives

$$\frac{Wv_B{}^2}{gr} = W \cos \theta$$

$$v_B{}^2 = gr \cos \theta$$

From the equation of velocity in a vertical curve

$$v_B{}^2 = v_A{}^2 + 2gh = 0 + 2g(r - r \cos \theta)$$

If the above equations are combined,

$$gr \cos \theta = 2g(r - r \cos \theta)$$

$$\cos \theta = 2 - 2 \cos \theta$$

$$\cos \theta = \tfrac{2}{3}$$

$$\theta = 48.2°$$

Problems

1. A 12-lb. body is rotating in a vertical circle at the end of a 3-ft. cord. Determine the velocity at the top of the path if the tension in the cord at that point is 10 lb.   What minimum velocity must the body have at the top to keep it in its circular path?   *Ans.* 13.3 ft. per sec.; 9.83 ft. per sec.

2. Starting from rest at the top of the incline, a man and car weighing 300 lb. move down the incline and around the loop-the-loop of 12 ft. radius shown in Fig. 272. Assuming friction to be negligible, determine the normal pressure on the car at B and at C.   *Ans.* 300 lb.; 1650 lb.

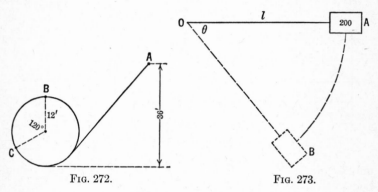

FIG. 272.   FIG. 273.

3. A 200-lb. body attached to a cable of length l is released from rest in position A, Fig. 273, and allowed to swing down. Compute the angle θ at which the tension in the cable will be 450 lb.   *Ans.* 48.6°.

4. Compute the strength of the cable in Prob. 3 if it breaks when $\theta = 60°$.
                                            Ans. 520 lb.

5. The two ropes supporting an ordinary swing are each 15 ft. long and have an ultimate tensile strength of 400 lb. each. What is the factor of safety of the ropes when a 100-lb. boy swings to 45° on each side of the vertical?
                                            Ans. 5.04.

Art. 69. Motion of Projectiles; Air Resistance Neglected.

The motion of a projectile is actually influenced not only by gravity but by such other factors as air friction, wind, rotation of the projectile due to rifling of the barrel, etc. Air friction, in turn, depends on the velocity of the projectile, its size, and its shape. A general solution may be made by neglecting all influences except gravity; this is equivalent to considering the projectile as moving without rotation in a vacuum. The general solution may then be modified to account for any of the other influences affecting the motion.

The general solution is conveniently made by treating independently the vertical and horizontal components of the motion. In Fig. 274 is shown the path or trajectory of a projectile which starts from point A with initial velocity v_0 at angle α with the horizontal. The initial velocity v_0 is shown resolved into its vertical and horizontal components $v_y = v_0 \sin \alpha$, and $v_x = v_0 \cos \alpha$. Since no horizontal force is acting, the horizontal component of the velocity remains constant. The vertical motion is affected

Fig. 274.

only by gravity and therefore is the same as that of a freely falling body. Thus for any point C in the path,

$$x = v_x \cdot t = v_0 t \cos \alpha$$

$$y = v_y t - \tfrac{1}{2} g t^2 = v_0 t \sin \alpha - \tfrac{1}{2} g t^2$$

If the time t is eliminated from the above equations, the equation of the trajectory or path is obtained

$$y = x \tan \alpha - \frac{g x^2}{2 v_0^2 \cos^2 \alpha}$$

This will be seen to be the equation of a parabola with vertical axis.

For the point D in the trajectory, $x = d$ and $y = 0$. If these values are substituted in the above equation of the trajectory, the horizontal range d of the projectile is obtained

$$d = \frac{2 v_0^2 \cos^2 \alpha \tan \alpha}{g} = \frac{v_0^2 \sin 2\alpha}{g}$$

The maximum height h to which the projectile rises is obtained from the equation $v^2 = v_0^2 + 2gh$ for a freely falling body. Since, at the top of the path, the vertical component of the velocity is zero, $v = 0$, and

$$h = \frac{v_0^2 \sin^2 \alpha}{2g}$$

By considering separately the vertical and horizontal components of the motion, many projectile problems may be solved without use of the special formulas developed in this article.

Example

A projectile has an initial velocity of 1500 ft. per sec., at an angle of 30° above the horizontal. Determine (a) the maximum height; (b) the horizontal distance traveled in reaching a target at 2000-ft. height; (c) the magnitude and inclination of the velocity on striking the target; (d) the equation of the trajectory.

Solution: In the trajectory shown in Fig. 275, A is the starting point, B is the point of maximum height, and C is the target. The initial

FIG. 275.

velocity at A is resolved into vertical and horizontal components, v_y and v_x.

$$v_y = 1500 \sin 30° = 750 \text{ ft. per sec.}$$

$$v_x = 1500 \cos 30° = 1300 \text{ ft. per sec.}$$

(a) *Maximum Height.* The maximum height h at B is computed from the equation of a freely falling body, $v^2 = v_0^2 + 2gh$. Since the vertical component of the velocity at B is zero, the equation becomes

$$0 = (750)^2 + 2(-32.2)h$$

$$h = 8740 \text{ ft.}$$

(b) *Range.* To determine the range d, the time, t_{AC}, from A to C is first computed from the equation of a freely falling body, $s = v_o t + \frac{1}{2}gt^2$. In this case, $s = 2000$ ft. and the equation becomes

$$2000 = 750t_{AC} + \frac{1}{2}(-32.2)t_{AC}^2$$

$$t_{AC} = 43.7 \text{ sec.}$$

Since the horizontal component of the initial velocity remains constant,

$$d = v_x \cdot t_{AC} = 1300 \times 43.7 = 56{,}800 \text{ ft.}$$

(c) *Velocity at C.* The magnitude of the velocity at C may be obtained from the equation of velocity in a vertical curved path, Art. 68.

$$v_C{}^2 = v_A{}^2 + 2gh = (1500)^2 + 2(-32.2)(2000)$$

$$v_C = 1460 \text{ ft. per sec.}$$

Since the horizontal component of the velocity at C is the same as that at A, the angle of inclination may be found as follows:

$$\theta = \cos^{-1} \frac{v_x}{v_C} = \cos^{-1} \frac{1300}{1460} = 27°$$

(d) *Equation of the Trajectory.* If x and y are coordinates of any point in the path and t is the time required to travel from A to this point, then

$$x = v_x t = 1300t$$

$$y = v_y t + \tfrac{1}{2} g t^2 = 750t + \tfrac{1}{2}(-32.2)t^2$$

By elimination of t from the two equations above, the equation of the trajectory is found to be

$$y = 0.577x - 0.00000953x^2$$

Problems

1. A gun fires a projectile with an initial velocity of 1800 ft. per sec. at an angle of 10° above the horizontal. Compute the range.
Ans. 34,400 ft.

2. An airplane drops a bomb from a height of 1000 ft. while traveling at 100 mi. per hr. How far in front of this position will the bomb strike?
Ans. 1160 ft.

3. A ball is thrown with an initial velocity of 50 ft. per sec. at an angle of 30° above the horizontal from a point 5 ft. above the ground. At what height will it strike a wall 15 ft. away?   *Ans.* 11.7 ft.

4. A ball is thrown from a tower 200 ft. high with an initial velocity of 100 ft. per sec. at an angle of 45° above the horizontal. When and where will it strike the ground?   *Ans.* 6.34 sec.; 448 ft.

5. A block starts from rest at the top and slides down a 30° incline 20 ft. long for which the coefficient of friction is 0.2. How far out from the foot of the incline will it strike a surface 15 ft. below?   *Ans.* 12.4 ft.

6. Determine the theoretical angle at which a projectile should be fired to obtain maximum range.   *Ans.* 45°.

Art. 70. Rotation. Motion of *rotation* is a special case of plane curvilinear motion in which the particle moves in a path of constant radius. A line through the center of the path and normal to its plane is called the axis of rotation.

The angle through which the radius vector to the particle moves as the particle changes position is called the *angular displacement*.

FIG. 276.

It may be measured in any convenient angular units, such as degrees, revolutions, or radians. It is usually necessary to express the angular displacement in radians, however, when its relation to other quantities is involved. Since an angle may be expressed as the ratio of one distance to another (arc/radius), angular displacement has no dimensions. In Fig. 276, in rotating from A to B, the angular displacement of the particle is θ radians. The linear distance traveled along the arc is s. The relation between the linear and angular distances traveled is expressed by

$$s = r \cdot \theta$$

Angular velocity is defined as the time rate of change of angular displacement. If the angular velocity, denoted by ω, is variable, its instantaneous value is

$$\omega = \frac{d\theta}{dt} \approx T^{-1}$$

If the angular velocity is constant, then

$$\omega = \frac{\theta}{t}$$

The more common units of angular velocity are revolutions per minute (r.p.m.) and radians per second. It is usually necessary to express angular velocity in radians per second if its relation to other quantities is involved.

The relation of angular velocity to the corresponding linear velocity tangent to the path is obtained from the equation $s = r\theta$ by differentiation.

$$\frac{ds}{dt} = r \frac{d\theta}{dt}$$

$$v = r\omega$$

Since angular velocity involves both magnitude and direction it is a vector quantity and, as such, is subject to the processes and laws governing other vector quantities. The vector representing angular velocity is parallel to the axis of rotation.

Angular acceleration is defined as the time rate of change of angular velocity. If the angular acceleration, denoted by α, is variable, its instantaneous value is

$$\alpha = \frac{d\omega}{dt} = \frac{d^2\theta}{dt^2} \approx T^{-2}$$

If the angular acceleration is constant, then

$$\alpha = \frac{\omega - \omega_0}{t}$$

Angular acceleration is usually expressed in radians per second per second, although other units, such as revolutions per minute per second are sometimes used. Since angular acceleration involves both magnitude and direction it is a vector quantity and, like angular velocity, is represented by a vector parallel to the axis of rotation.

By differentiation of the equation $v = r\omega$, the relation between tangential and angular acceleration is obtained.

$$\frac{dv}{dt} = r\frac{d\omega}{dt}$$

$$a_t = r\alpha$$

From Art. 64, $a_n = v^2/r$. Since $v = r\omega$,

$$a_n = r\omega^2$$

If dt is eliminated from the equations, $\omega = d\theta/dt$ and $\alpha = d\omega/dt$ the following relation results.

$$\omega d\omega = \alpha d\theta$$

This equation may be integrated if α can be expressed in terms of θ. It is therefore useful in determining the change in angular velocity in certain cases involving variable angular acceleration.

Problems

1. Make the following conversions: (a) 5 revolutions to radians; (b) 240° to radians; (c) 10 radians to revolutions; (d) $\frac{1}{3}\pi$ radians to degrees.

Ans. (a) 10π rad.; (b) $4\pi/3 = 4.19$ rad.; (c) 1.59 rev.; (d) 60°.

2. Make the following conversions: (a) 60 r.p.m. to radians per sec.; (b) 4.5 radians per sec. to r.p.m.   Ans (a) $2\pi = 6.28$ rad. per sec.; (b) 43.0 r.p.m.

3. A wheel 3 ft. in diameter rotates at 120 r.p.m.   Determine the tangential linear velocity of a point on the rim.   Ans. 18.8 ft. per sec.

4. If the speed of rotation of the wheel in Prob. 3 is increased at a uniform rate to 240 r.p.m. in 10 sec., compute: (a) the angular acceleration; (b) the tangential acceleration of a point on the rim; (c) the normal acceleration of a point on the rim for 240 r.p.m.

Ans. (a) 1.26 rad. per sec.²; (b) 1.88 ft. per sec.²; (c) 948 ft. per sec.²

5. Two pulleys of 12-in. and 30-in. diameters, respectively, are connected by a belt.   If the linear velocity of a point on the belt is 15 ft. per sec., and the belt does not slip, determine: (a) the angular velocity of each pulley; (b) the normal acceleration of a point on the rim of each pulley.

Ans. (a) 30 rad. per sec.;   12 rad. per sec.;
(b) 450 ft. per sec.²; 180 ft. per sec.²

Fig. 277.

6. A slender rod of length $l = 3$ ft., Fig. 277, is mounted on a horizontal axis of rotation through one end.   The rod is released from rest in a vertical position above the axis and allowed to rotate under the influence of gravity alone.   It may be shown (Art. 80) that its angular acceleration for any angle θ is given by the expression, $\alpha = (3g/2l) \sin \theta$.   Determine the angular velocity when $\theta = 180°$. (Note that the angular acceleration is variable.)   Ans. 8.02 rad. per sec.

Art. 71. Uniformly Accelerated Rotational Motion.
It was shown in Art. 70 that, when angular acceleration is constant or uniform,

$$a = \frac{\omega - \omega_0}{t} \tag{1}$$

Under the same conditions, the average angular velocity may be expressed as

$$\omega_{av.} = \tfrac{1}{2}(\omega + \omega_0)$$

The angular displacement will then be

$$\theta = \omega_{av.} \cdot t = \tfrac{1}{2}(\omega + \omega_0)t \tag{2}$$

If t is eliminated from equations (1) and (2), the following relation is obtained:

$$\omega^2 = \omega_0^2 + 2a\theta \tag{3}$$

If ω is eliminated from equations (1) and (2), the resulting relation is

$$\theta = \omega_0 t + \tfrac{1}{2}at^2 \qquad (4)$$

The above equations, (1) to (4), are known as the equations of uniformly accelerated rotational motion. They are analogous to the equations of uniformly accelerated rectilinear motion as stated in Art. 59.

Problems

1. Derive equations (1), (3), and (4) above by integration of the equations $\omega = d\theta/dt$, and $\alpha = d\omega/dt$.

2. Derive equations (1) to (4) above from the corresponding equations of Art. 59 by use of the relations $s = r\theta$, $v = r\omega$, and $a_t = r\alpha$.

3. A flywheel is brought from rest up to a speed of 600 r.p.m. in 1.5 min. with uniform acceleration. Determine the angular acceleration and the number of revolutions made in coming up to speed.

Ans. 0.698 rad. per sec.²; 450 rev.

4. A shaft has an initial angular velocity of 30 r.p.m. and is accelerated uniformly at the rate of 2 rev. per min. per sec. Determine the angular velocity at the end of 30 sec. and the number of revolutions made in this time.

Ans. 90 r.p.m.; 30 rev.

5. A flywheel rotating at 300 r.p.m. makes 120 revolutions in coming to rest. Determine the angular acceleration and the time to come to rest.

Ans. 0.655 rad. per sec.²; 48 sec.

Art. 72. Simple Harmonic Motion; Auxiliary Circle Method.

Motion of a particle in a straight-line path with an acceleration which is proportional to the displacement from some fixed point in the path and oppositely directed is called *simple harmonic motion*. The motion is defined mathematically by the equation

$$a = -\, k\, s$$

where s denotes the displacement, k is the constant of proportionality, and the negative sign indicates that acceleration and displacement are opposite in direction. This type of motion is involved in the vibration of elastic bodies.

The development of the equations and the solution of problems in simple harmonic motion are most conveniently accomplished by the use of the auxiliary circle. This method depends on the fact that if a point moves with constant speed in a circular path, its projection on the diameter of the circle moves with simple harmonic

motion, as will now be shown.   In Fig. 278, the point P moves
with uniform angular velocity ω in a circular path of radius r.   Its
projection P' on the diameter moves back and forth across the
diameter AOB.   If displacements are measured from the axis OY,
the angular displacement of P is θ and the linear displacement of
P' is s.   Since $\theta = \omega t$,

$$\mathbf{s} = r \sin \theta = \mathbf{r} \sin \omega t$$

The linear velocity of P is tangent to the circular path and is
given by

$$v_t = r\omega$$

The linear velocity of P' is

$$\mathbf{v} = ds/dt = \mathbf{r\omega} \cos \omega t$$

FIG. 278   FIG. 279.

This will be seen from Fig. 279 (a) to be the projection of v_t upon
the diameter.   The linear acceleration of P is normal to the circular path and is given by

$$a_n = r\omega^2$$

The acceleration of P' is

$$\mathbf{a} = dv/dt = -\ \mathbf{r\omega^2} \sin \omega t$$

This is seen from Fig. 279 (b) to be the projection of a_n upon the
diameter.   Since $r \sin \omega t = s$,

$$a = -\ \omega^2 s$$

Since ω is constant, the above equation conforms to the original mathematical definition and the motion of P' is thus shown to be simple harmonic.

From the equation $s = r \sin \omega t$, the time t to travel from O to P' is

$$t = \frac{1}{\omega} \sin^{-1} \frac{s}{r}$$

The *period* T is the time required for one complete oscillation of P'. This is obviously the same as the time required for one revolution of P. Hence

$$T = \frac{2\pi}{\omega}$$

The *frequency* n is the number of complete oscillations in 1 sec. and is therefore the reciprocal of the period.

$$n = \frac{\omega}{2\pi} = \frac{1}{T}$$

The *amplitude* is one-half the length of the path and is thus equal to the radius of the auxiliary circle.

Although simple harmonic motion is actually a rectilinear motion and might logically be treated under that heading in Chap. VIII, the use of the auxiliary circle and the equations of rotation simplify the treatment to such an extent as to justify its consideration as a topic in curvilinear motion.

Example 1

A particle oscillates with simple harmonic motion for which the amplitude is 3 in. and the period is $\frac{1}{3}$ sec. Determine the velocity and acceleration of the particle when its displacement from the center of the path is 1 in. Determine the time since it was at the center.

Solution: The auxiliary circle with radius of 3 in. $= \frac{1}{4}$ ft. is shown in Fig. 280; P' represents the oscillating particle at 1 in. $= \frac{1}{12}$ ft. from the center O, and P is the corresponding point on the circle. The angular velocity of P is

Fig. 280.

$$\omega = 2\pi/T = 2\pi/\tfrac{1}{3} = 6\pi \text{ rad. per sec.}$$

The tangential linear velocity of P is

$$v_t = r\omega = \tfrac{1}{4} \times 6\pi = 4.71 \text{ ft. per sec.}$$

and its linear acceleration in the normal direction is

$$a_n = r\omega^2 = \tfrac{1}{4} \times (6\pi)^2 = 88.8 \text{ ft. per sec.}^2$$

The angular displacement θ is

$$\theta = \sin^{-1}\frac{\frac{1}{12}}{\frac{1}{4}} = \sin^{-1}\tfrac{1}{3} = 19.5°$$

The velocity and acceleration of P' are now obtained by projecting v_t and a_n upon the diameter

$$v = v_t \cos \theta = 4.71 \cos 19.5° = 4.44 \text{ ft. per sec.}$$

$$a = a_n \sin \theta = 88.8 \sin 19.5° = 29.6 \text{ ft. per sec.}^2$$

The time from O to P' is the same as that required for rotation of P through angle θ. Hence,

$$t = \theta/\omega = \frac{19.5 \times \pi/180}{6\pi} = 0.018 \text{ sec.}$$

Example 2

A 30-lb. weight suspended from a spring whose scale is 20 lb. per in. is set into vibration. Determine the period of vibration.

FIG. 281.

Solution: Since the force required to deflect a spring (within its elastic limit) is proportional to the displacement, and since the acceleration is proportional to the force, it follows that the acceleration of the vibrating weight will be proportional to its displacement and the motion is simple harmonic.

Let O, Fig. 281, represent the equilibrium position of the suspended weight. If the spring is now deflected downward any distance r inches, the force required will be $20r$ pounds. When this force is removed the weight will be set into vibration. At the instant of release, the weight is acted upon by an unbalanced force of $20r$ pounds and will thus have an instantaneous acceleration

$$a = \frac{Fg}{W} = \frac{20rg}{30} \text{ ft. per sec.}^2$$

This acceleration corresponds to the acceleration a_n as shown on the auxiliary circle. Since $a_n = r\omega^2$

$$\omega^2 = \frac{a_n}{r} = \frac{20rg/30}{r/12} = 8g = 258$$

$$\omega = \sqrt{258} = 16.1 \text{ rad. per sec.}$$

$$T = 2\pi/\omega = 2\pi/16.1 = 0.39 \text{ sec.}$$

Problems

1. The amplitude of a simple harmonic motion is 1.5 ft. and the period is 1 sec. Compute the maximum velocity and the maximum acceleration.

Ans. 9.42 ft. per sec.; 59.2 ft. per sec.²

2. The amplitude of a simple harmonic motion is 10 in. and the period is 0.5 sec. Determine the position of the moving particle, its velocity, and its acceleration 0.2 sec. after leaving the end of the path.

Ans. 18.1 in. from end; 6.15 ft. per sec.; 106 ft. per sec.²

3. A 100-lb. weight is suspended from a spring whose scale is 200 lb. per in. and then caused to oscillate. Determine the period of oscillation.

Ans. 0.226 sec.

4. What weight, suspended from a spring whose scale is 60 lb. per in., will oscillate with a period of 1 sec.? *Ans.* 588 lb.

5. The drive wheels of a locomotive are 4 ft. in diameter and the crank radius is 1 ft. If the speed of the locomotive is 45 mi. per hr., determine the maximum velocity and the maximum acceleration of the piston with respect to the cylinder, assuming that the connecting rod is of such length that the motion of the piston may be considered as approximately simple harmonic.

Ans. 33 ft. per sec.; 1090 ft. per sec.²

Supplementary Problems

1. At what speed in revolutions per minute will an object placed at 3 ft. from the center of a horizontal rotating platform start to slide off if the coefficient of friction is 0.4? *Ans.* 19.8 r.p.m.

2. Determine the length l of the arms of the conical pendulum governor shown in Fig. 282 if the angle θ is to be 30° when the speed of rotation is 90 r.p.m. Assume the weight of the arms to be negligible. Compute the tension in each arm if each ball weighs 20 lb.

Ans. 0.419 ft.; 23.1 lb.

3. If the length l of the arms of the governor in Prob. 2 is increased to 2 ft., determine, for the same speed of rotation, the angle θ and the tension in the arms. *Ans.* 79.6°; 110 lb.

4. Determine the angle at which a highway curve of 300-ft. radius should

Fig. 282.

be superelevated for a speed of 60 mi. per hr. to prevent skidding if the coefficient of friction is 0.5.   *Ans.* 12.1°.

5. Compute the lateral pressure on the wheels of a 3000-lb. car with velocity of 45 mi. per hr. on the curve of Prob. 4.   *Ans.* 694 lb.

6. What is the maximum speed with which a car can travel round the curve of Prob. 4 without skidding if the surface is wet, reducing the coefficient of friction to 0.3?   *Ans.* 49.8 mi. per hr.

7. A car starts from rest at the top of an incline and must reach the bottom with sufficient velocity to enable it to travel round a vertical " loop-the-loop " of 16-ft. diameter without falling. Compute the minimum height of the incline, assuming friction to be negligible.   *Ans.* 20.0 ft.

8. Compute the maximum diameter of a " loop-the-loop " around which a car can travel without falling after starting from rest at the top of an incline 30 ft. high.   Neglect friction.   *Ans.* 24 ft.

FIG. 283.

9. A small block starts from rest at A and slides down the frictionless arc AB, Fig. 283. Determine the distance d and the magnitude and direction of the velocity of striking at C.

Ans. 11.6 ft.; 22.7 ft. per sec. at 50.5° with horizontal.

10. A block with initial velocity of 10 ft. per sec. at A slides down the frictionless chute AB, Fig. 284. Compute the distance d.

Ans. d = 11.2 ft.

11. A block starts from rest at the top of a smooth sphere.   At what angle

FIG. 284.

from the starting point will it leave the surface of the sphere? *Ans.* 48.2°.

12. A ball thrown horizontally from the top of a building 200 ft. high strikes the ground at 100 ft. away.   Compute the velocity with which it was thrown.

Ans. 28.5 ft. per sec.

13. A gun located in a valley fires a projectile with muzzle velocity of 1000 ft. per sec. at 45° with the horizontal. How far away on a plain at 400-ft. elevation above the valley will the projectile strike? To what height does the projectile rise? *Ans.* 5.8 mi.; 7760 ft.

14. What should be the angle of firing for a projectile with muzzle velocity of 1200 ft. per sec. to strike a target 8 mi. away on the same level?
Ans. 35.4° above horizontal.

15. If the target is 2000 ft. away horizontally and 1000 ft. higher than the gun, determine the angle of elevation necessary when firing a projectile with muzzle velocity of 1500 ft. per sec. *Ans.* 27.4°.

16. A weight of 50 lb., suspended from a spring, oscillates with a frequency of 2 vibrations per second. Compute the scale of the spring.
Ans. 20.4 lb. per in.

17. A point moves with a simple harmonic motion such that its velocity is 4 ft. per sec. when it is 3 in. from the center of its path, and 3 ft. per sec. when it is 4 in. from the center. Determine the amplitude and period.
Ans. 5 in.; 0.523 sec.

CHAPTER X

WORK, ENERGY, AND POWER

Art. 73. Work. When a change in the position of a body is effected in opposition to a resisting force, *work* is done. The measure of the amount of work done by or against a force is the product of the force and the displacement, provided the force is constant and acting in the direction of the displacement.

$$U = \text{work} = \mathbf{F} \cdot \mathbf{s} \approx M L^2 T^{-2}$$

If the force and displacement are not collinear, then work is done by the component of the force in the direction of the displacement. Thus, if the force acts at angle θ with the direction of displacement,

$$U = Fs \cos \theta$$

If the force is variable, the work done during an increment of displacement may be expressed as $F \cdot ds$ and the total work is then obtained by means of an integral:

$$U = \int F \, ds$$

In order to evaluate the integral, the force must be expressed as a function of displacement. Work may be expressed in terms of any units of force and displacement. The most frequently used unit in engineering is the foot-pound.

Work does not involve a sense of direction and is therefore a scalar quantity. Thus the total work done on a body or system of bodies may be obtained by algebraic addition of the work done by the various forces acting. It is customary to regard the work as positive when the force and displacement are in the same direction, and as negative when force and displacement are oppositely directed.

Work may be represented graphically by plotting on rectangular axes the values of force and corresponding displacement.

Thus, in Fig. 285 (*a*) is shown the work diagram of a force varying inversely as the displacement. Since work is the product of force and displacement, the shaded area represents the amount of work done in a change of displacement from s_1 to s_2. The indicator card of a steam engine, shown in Fig. 285 (*b*), is another example of the graphical representation of work. The shaded area, representing work, is determined by use of a planimeter.

(a)   (b)

Fig. 285.

In lowering or raising a body, work is done by or against gravity and is determined by the product of the weight of the body and the vertical distance the body is moved. Thus:

$$U = Wh$$

Sometimes all portions of an object are not moved the same vertical distance, and then the work is determined by summation of the amounts of work done on different parts of the body as follows,

$$U = \int h \cdot dw = W \cdot \bar{h}$$

where $\bar{h}$ is the vertical distance through which the center of gravity moves.

Example

A tank of hemispherical shape, 6 ft. in diameter, is full of water. How much work is done in emptying the tank if all the water must be pumped up over the edge of the tank?

Solution: The volume of water is:

$$V = \tfrac{2}{3}\pi r^3 = \tfrac{2}{3}\pi(3)^3 = 56.5 \text{ cu. ft.}$$

The weight of the water is

$$W = 56.5 \times 62.5 = 3530 \text{ lb.}$$

The center of gravity of the hemispherical volume is located at a distance $\bar{h}$ from the top, where

$$\bar{h} = \tfrac{3}{8}r = \tfrac{3}{8} \times 3 = 1.125 \text{ ft.}$$

The work done is thus:

$$U = W\bar{h} = 3530 \times 1.125 = 3970 \text{ ft-lb.}$$

Problems

1. Show that the work done by a constant torque of T foot-pounds which produces an angular displacement θ in radians is $T\theta$ foot-pounds.

2. A 150-ft. length of cable weighing 1.6 lb. per ft. is suspended from a drum. How much work is done in winding up 135 ft. of the cable on the drum?   *Ans.* 17,800 ft.-lb.

3. The excavation for the basement of a building is 30 ft. long, 20 ft. wide, and 10 ft. deep. The first 4 ft. below the surface consists of gravel weighing 140 lb. per cu. ft.; the last 6 ft. is clay weighing 100 lb. per cu. ft. Compute the work done in lifting the excavated material to the surface.
                    Ans. 3,190,000 ft-lb.

4. A chain 100 ft. long and weighing 3 lb. per ft. passes over a pulley with 80 ft. hanging on one side and 20 ft. on the other. Compute the work done against gravity if the pulley is rotated until 50 ft. of chain hangs on each side.   *Ans.* 2700 ft-lb.

5. Compute the total work done by a locomotive in pulling a 50-ton car a distance of 4000 ft. up a $\frac{1}{2}$ per cent grade with uniform velocity, if train resistance is 6 lb. per ton.   *Ans.* 3,200,000 ft-lb.

6. Determine the work done in punching a 9/16-in. diameter hole through a $\frac{3}{8}$-in. thick steel plate whose ultimate shearing strength is 40,000 lb. per sq. in. Assume that, during the punching operation, the force exerted by the punch varies as the thickness of material remaining to be punched out.
                    Ans. 414 ft-lb.

7. A belt drives a pulley of 2-ft. diameter. If the tensions on the two sides of the belt are 400 lb. and 200 lb. respectively, determine the work done in 60 revolutions of the pulley.   *Ans.* 75,400 ft-lb.

Art. 74. Energy. *Energy* is the ability to do work and is measured by the amount of work a body is capable of doing in changing from some given condition to some standard condition. Energy is expressed in terms of work units. There are various forms of energy, but those of particular importance in mechanics are *potential* energy due to position, and *kinetic* energy due to motion.

A body in a position above some standard reference level is capable of doing work in falling from the higher to the lower position and is therefore said to possess potential energy. If h is the difference in elevation, the potential energy is

$$\text{P.E.} = \mathbf{W} \cdot \mathbf{h} \approx M L^2 T^{-2}$$

A body in motion is capable of doing work in coming to rest and is said to possess kinetic energy. Some resultant resisting force $F = Wa/g$ is necessary to bring a body having rectilinear motion to rest. The kinetic energy of the moving body is equal to the work that must be done by this force in bringing the body to rest. Therefore, the kinetic energy of translation is

$$K.E. = U = \int -F \, ds$$

$$= \int -\frac{Wa}{g} \, ds = -\frac{W}{g} \int a \, ds$$

$$= -\frac{W}{g} \int_v^0 v \, dv$$

$$\mathbf{K.E.} = \frac{1}{2} \frac{\mathbf{W}}{\mathbf{g}} \mathbf{v}^2 = \frac{1}{2} \mathbf{M} \mathbf{v}^2 \approx M L^2 T^{-2}$$

Problems

1. A cylindrical tank 6 ft. in diameter and 10 ft. deep is full of water. Determine the potential energy of the water with respect to a surface 15 ft. below the bottom of the tank. *Ans.* 353,000 ft-lb.

2. Compute the kinetic energy of a 3000-lb. car when its velocity is (a) 30 mi. per hr.; (b) 60 mi. per hr. *Ans.* 90,200 ft-lb.; 361,000 ft-lb.

3. Water leaves a nozzle of 4-in. diameter with a velocity of 50 ft. per sec. Determine the kinetic energy of the quantity of water passing through the nozzle in 1 sec. *Ans.* 10,600 ft-lb.

4. In firing an 800-lb. projectile with a muzzle velocity of 1200 ft. per sec., a 100,000-lb. gun recoils with an initial velocity of 9.6 ft. per sec. Compute the kinetic energy imparted to the gun and to the projectile by the explosion. *Ans.* 143,000 ft-lb.; 17,900,000 ft-lb.

Art. 75. Work-Energy Relations for Translation; Constant Forces. A body in motion possesses a certain amount of kinetic energy, depending on its mass and velocity. If any forces act on the body in the direction of motion, positive work will be done, the effect of which will be to accelerate the body, thus increasing the velocity and the kinetic energy. The increase in kinetic energy must equal the positive work done. Similarly, negative work will be done by forces resisting the motion, the effect of which will be to decelerate the body, thus decreasing the velocity and the kinetic energy. The decrease in kinetic energy must equal the negative work done by these forces.

In any operation where a moving body is acted upon simultaneously by both driving and resisting forces, the relation between the final and initial values of the kinetic energy may be expressed as follows:

Initial K.E. + Positive work − Negative work = Final K.E.

This statement will be referred to subsequently as the work-energy equation. It is particularly useful in solving problems involving force, velocity, and displacement.

Example

A 600-lb. block on a 30° incline is connected to a 150-lb. counterweight hanging vertically from a cable running over a pulley as shown in Fig. 286. The coefficient of friction between block and incline is 0.2. Neglecting the mass of the pulley and its axle friction, determine the velocity of the blocks after moving 20 ft. from rest.

FIG. 286.

Solution: The initial kinetic energy of the system is zero. Positive work is done by gravity acting on the 600-lb. block.

$$\text{Positive work} = 600 \times 20 \sin 30° = 6000 \text{ ft-lb.}$$

Negative work is done by friction acting on the 600-lb. block, and by gravity acting on the counterweight.

$$\text{Negative work} = 0.2 \,(600 \cos 30°) \times 20 + 150 \times 20 = 5080 \text{ ft-lb.}$$

The final kinetic energy of the system in terms of the unknown velocity v is:

$$K.E. = \frac{1}{2} \cdot \frac{600}{32.2} v^2 + \frac{1}{2} \frac{150}{32.2} v^2 = \frac{1}{2} \frac{750}{32.2} v^2$$

The above items are now combined into the work-energy equation:

$$0 + 6000 - 5080 = \frac{1}{2} \frac{750}{32.2} v^2$$

$$v = 8.9 \text{ ft. per sec.}$$

The solution of the above example should be compared with its solution in Art. 62 by means of D'Alembert's principle.

Problems

1. A 1000-ton train is hauled up a $1\frac{1}{2}$ per cent grade. Train resistance is 10 lb. per ton. Compute the drawbar pull required to change the speed from 10 mi. per hr. to 30 mi. per hr. in a distance of 1 mile.

Ans. 50,100 lb.

2. A block, starting from rest, slides 20 ft. down a 45° slope, then 10 ft. along a level surface, and then up a 30° incline until it comes to rest again. If the coefficient of friction is 0.15 for all three surfaces, compute the total distance traveled.

Ans. 46.7 ft.

Fig. 287.

3. Determine the velocity of the 200-lb. block in Fig. 287 after moving 12 ft. from rest, if the coefficient of friction is 0.2. Compute the cable tension. *Ans.* 19.1 ft. per sec.; 229 lb.

4. If car resistance is 8 lb. per ton, in what distance will the cable car of Fig. 288 attain a velocity of 15 mi. per hr.? *Ans.* 114 ft.

Fig. 288.

5. If a 20-ton car has a velocity of 30 mi. per hr. down a $\frac{1}{2}$ per cent grade, what normal brake shoe pressure on each of the eight wheels is required to bring the car to rest in a distance of 500 ft., assuming each wheel to carry one-eighth of the load and the coefficient of kinetic friction between wheel and shoe to be 0.3? *Ans.* 1090 lb.

Art. 76. Work-Energy Relations for Translation; Variable Forces.

As pointed out in Art. 73, the work done by a variable force may be determined by means of the integral $\int F\ ds$, provided that the force can be expressed as a function of displacement.

The helical spring furnishes an illustration of variable force action, the force acting at any instant being proportional to the displacement as long as the elastic limit of the material is not exceeded. The scale of a spring is the force required to produce unit deflection. If C is the scale of a spring expressed in pounds per inch, as is customary, and s is the displacement in inches, then the work done in producing this displacement is

$$U = \int F \, ds = \int_0^s Cs \, ds = \frac{Cs^2}{2} \text{ in-lb.} = \frac{Cs^2}{24} \text{ ft-lb.}$$

This expression may then be introduced into the work-energy equation.

Example

A 50-lb. block is projected up a 30° incline by means of a spring whose scale is 200 lb. per in. The coefficient of friction on the incline is 0.2. If the spring was given an initial deflection of 12 in., determine the velocity of the block after moving 30 ft. up the slope.

Solution: The initial kinetic energy of the block is zero. Positive work is done by the spring. Negative work is done by gravity and by friction. These items are shown in the following work-energy equation:

$$0 + \frac{200(12)^2}{24} - 50 \times 30 \sin 30° - 0.2 \, (50 \cos 30°) \times 30 = \frac{1}{2} \frac{50}{32.2} v^2$$

$$v = 15.6 \text{ ft. per sec.}$$

Problems

1. A 30-ton freight car strikes a bumping post, compressing a drawbar spring 4 in. If the scale of the spring is 200,000 lb. per in., what was the velocity of the car? *Ans.* 8.15 mi. per hr.

2. A 65-lb. weight falls 15 in. upon a spring whose scale is 20 lb. per in. Compute the maximum deflection of the spring. What velocity does the weight have when the deflection of the spring is 10 in.? *Ans.* 13.7 in.; 7.18 ft. per sec.

3. If a gun weighing 25,000 lb. has an initial recoil velocity of 10 ft. per sec., what must be the scale of a set of springs which will limit the distance of recoil to 2 ft.? *Ans.* 1620 lb. per in.

4. A 30-lb. block slides 2 ft. down a 60° plane and strikes a 40-lb. spring. If the coefficient of friction on the plane is 0.25, compute the maximum deflection of the spring and distance the block will rebound up the plane. *Ans.* 5.75 in.; 1.86 ft.

5. A freight car weighing 50 tons is switched to a 2 per cent up-grade with a velocity of 15 mi. per hr. Car resistance is 9 lb. per ton. After moving 300 ft. up the grade the car strikes a bumper. If the drawbar spring has a scale of 20,000 lb. per in., how far will it deflect? *Ans.* 4.45 in.

Art. 77. Kinetic Energy of Rotation. To determine the kinetic energy of a rotating body, the expression for the kinetic energy of a differential portion is integrated between proper limits so as to include the entire body. In Fig. 289 is shown a rigid body rotating with angular velocity ω about an axis through point 0. The tangential linear velocity of a differential mass dM located at distance ρ from the axis of rotation is $v_t = \rho\omega$. The kinetic energy of the differential mass is then:

FIG. 289.

$$\tfrac{1}{2}dM\,v_t{}^2 = \tfrac{1}{2}dM\rho^2\omega^2$$

and the kinetic energy of the entire body becomes:

$$\textbf{K.E.} = \int \frac{1}{2}\,dM\rho^2\omega^2 = \frac{1}{2}\,\omega^2 \int \rho^2 dM = \frac{1}{2}\,\mathbf{I_0\omega^2}$$

The work-energy equation, as used in problems of translation, also applies to rotation.

FIG. 290.

Example

A windlass with a brake to control its motion is shown in Fig. 290. The rotating parts weigh 400 lb. and have a radius of gyration of 0.75 ft. The load suspended from the windlass has a downward velocity of 15 ft. per sec. before the brake is applied. If the coefficient of friction for the brake is 0.5, and axle friction is considered negligible, what normal pressure N on the brake is required to bring the load to rest in a distance of 40 ft?

Solution: The angular velocity of the windlass is

$$\omega = \frac{v}{r} = \frac{15}{\frac{1}{4}} = 60 \text{ rad. per sec.}$$

The moment of inertia of the windlass is

$$I = \frac{W}{g}\,k^2 = \frac{400}{32.2}\,(\tfrac{3}{4})^2 = \frac{225}{32.2}$$

Thus the initial kinetic energy of the windlass is

$$K.E. = \frac{1}{2} I\omega^2 = \frac{1}{2} \frac{225}{32.2} (60)^2 \text{ ft-lb.}$$

This kinetic energy added to that of the falling load constitutes the total initial kinetic energy of the system.

Positive work is done by gravity on the falling load. Negative work is done by the brake friction which operates through a distance obtained by multiplying the distance traveled by the load by the ratio of the two circumferences or radii. Thus, in this case, the brake friction operates through 160 ft. The final kinetic energy is zero.

The above quantities are now substituted in the work-energy equation:

$$\frac{1}{2} \frac{225}{32.2} (60)^2 + \frac{1}{2} \frac{1000}{32.2} (15)^2 + 1000 \times 40 - 0.5N \times 160 = 0$$
$$N = 701 \text{ lb.}$$

Problems

1. The rotating parts of the system shown in Fig. 291 weigh 300 lb. and have a radius of gyration of 1.5 ft. If the system is released from rest, compute the angular velocity after the 100-lb. body has moved 10 ft. Use $f = 0.3$ for the 150-lb. weight and neglect journal friction.   *Ans.* 60.9 r.p.m.

FIG. 291.   FIG. 292.

2. If the 150-lb. body of Fig. 291 hangs vertically, compute the revolutions per minute of the wheel after the 100-lb. body has moved 10 ft.

Ans. 34.6 r.p.m.

3. A cylinder of 4-ft. diameter weighing 200 lb. is attached to a horizontal axle through O, as shown in Fig. 292. If the cylinder is released from rest in the position indicated, with what angular velocity will it pass through a position (*a*) 90° farther on; (*b*) 180° farther on?

Ans. 4.64 rad. per sec.; 6.55 rad. per sec.

4. A 1000-lb. load is suspended from a cable wrapped around a pulley of 1-ft. diameter which is attached to a flywheel as shown in Fig. 293. The total weight of the rotating parts is 400 lb., and the radius of gyration is 1.5 ft. If the load is being raised with a velocity of 20 ft. per sec., how much farther will it rise if the power is cut off? Neglect friction of bearings.

Ans. 28.6 ft.

FIG. 293.   FIG. 294.

5. The motion of the system shown in Fig. 294 is controlled by a band brake. The weight of the rotating drum is 400 lb. and its radius of gyration is $\frac{3}{4}$ ft. The coefficient of band friction is $\frac{1}{3}$. The coefficient of kinetic friction for the incline is 0.2. If the system starts from rest, what will be the velocity of the 3000-lb. block after moving 10 ft? *Ans.* 8.80 ft. per sec.

6. A solid steel cylinder 4 ft. in diameter and 2 ft. long is keyed to a 6-in.-diameter shaft supported in bearings on each side of the cylinder. The coefficient of friction between axle and bearings is 0.015. If the cylinder has angular velocity of 60 r.p.m. when power is cut off how many revolutions will it make in coming to rest? *Ans.* 52 rev.

Art. 78. Power. *Power* is the time rate of doing work. Thus,

$$\text{Power} = P = \frac{dU}{dt}$$

If power remains constant during a given operation, the above expression becomes

$$\mathbf{P} = \frac{\mathbf{U}}{\mathbf{t}} \approx ML^2T^{-3}$$

Power is expressed in terms of work and time units, two frequently used units being the foot-pound per second and the foot-pound per minute. A larger unit commonly employed is the horsepower, abbreviated hp., which consists of 550 ft-lb. per sec., or 33,000 ft-lb. per min.

Power may also be determined in terms of force and velocity as shown by the following relation,

$$\mathbf{P} = \frac{U}{t} = \frac{Fs}{t} = \mathbf{F} \cdot \mathbf{v} \approx ML^2T^{-3}$$

The ratio of the power output of a machine to the power input is called the efficiency of the machine.

Example 1

A turbine is driven by water supplied from a penstock of 2-ft. diameter under a head of 30 ft. Neglecting any friction losses, determine the horsepower theoretically available.

Solution: The velocity of the water leaving the penstock is given by:

$$v = \sqrt{2gh} = \sqrt{2 \times 32.2 \times 30} = 44 \text{ ft. per sec.}$$

The volume of water delivered in 1 sec. is

$$Q = Av = \pi(1)^2 \times 44 = 138 \text{ cu. ft.}$$

The weight of this volume of water is

$$W = 138 \times 62.5 = 8630 \text{ lb.}$$

The energy possessed by the above quantity of water may be computed either as potential energy:

$$P.E. = Wh = 8630 \times 30 = 259,000 \text{ ft-lb.}$$

or as kinetic energy:

$$K.E. = \frac{1}{2}\frac{W}{g}v^2 = \frac{1}{2}\frac{8630}{32.2}(44)^2 = 259,000 \text{ ft-lb.}$$

The horsepower theoretically available is then

$$hp. = \frac{U}{550t} = \frac{259,000}{550 \times 1} = 471.$$

Example 2

Compute the horsepower developed by a locomotive which pulls a train of 40 cars weighing 50 tons each at a velocity of 15 mi. per hr. up a 1 per cent grade, train resistance being 10 lb. per ton.

Solution: The total drawbar pull required to overcome gravity and train resistance is

$$F = 40 \times 50 \times 2000 \times 0.01 + 40 \times 50 \times 10 = 60,000 \text{ lb.}$$

The power is then

$$hp. = \frac{Fv}{550} = 60,000 \times \frac{22}{550} = 2400$$

Problems

1. If T is the torque in foot-pounds transmitted by a shaft and n is the speed of rotation in revolutions per minute, show that the horsepower transmitted is $2\pi nT/33,000$.

2. Compute the horsepower developed by a pump which fills a 20,000-gal. water tank in 2 hr. if the water must be raised 50 ft. to an intake at the top of the tank. *Ans.* 2.11 hp.

3. The speed of a 1000 ton train is increased from 15 mi. per hr. to 30 mi. per hr. in a distance of 1 mile up a 1 per cent grade. If train resistance is 8 lb. per ton, compute the maximum horsepower developed by the locomotive. *Ans.* 2920 hp.

4. A turbine is driven by a 1-in. diameter jet of water under a head of 600 ft. If the turbine has an efficiency of 90 per cent and is connected to a generator whose efficiency is 95 per cent, compute the power output of the generator in kilowatts. *Ans.* 46.6 kw.

5. The tensions on the two sides of a belt driving a pulley of 1.5-ft. diameter are 600 lb. and 200 lb. If the pulley has a speed of 300 r.p.m., what horsepower is being transmitted? *Ans.* 17.1 hp.

Fig. 295.

6. In Fig. 295 is shown a device called the Prony brake, used to determine the power output of an engine. It consists of a type of band brake which absorbs the energy supplied by the engine and converts it into heat by means of the friction between the band brake and a flywheel or pulley driven by the engine. The force P required to hold the brake in position is measured and the friction F of the band is then determined from the relation, $Pl = Fr$. Show that the horsepower developed is $\dfrac{2\pi n P l}{33,000}$ if n is the speed of rotation in revolutions per minute.

Supplementary Problems

1. A water tank is cylindrical in shape with a hemispherical bottom. The cylindrical portion has 12-ft. diameter and 5-ft. altitude. The tank is filled through its bottom, which is 40 ft. above the intake to the pump. Compute the work done by the pump in filling the tank.

Ans. 2,950,000 ft-lb.

2. If the pump used in filling the tank of Prob. 1 develops 2 hp., how long will it take to fill the tank?   *Ans.* 44.7 min.

3. Compute the horsepower of a pump which takes water from a pond 10 ft. below and delivers it from a pipe 3 in. in diameter with a velocity of 60 ft. per sec.   *Ans.* 22.1 hp.

4. A train of 40 cars weighing 20 tons each is running at a speed of 45 mi. per hr. on a level track. If train resistance is 10 lb. per ton, determine the drawbar pull and the horsepower being developed by the locomotive.

Ans. 8000 lb.; 960 hp.

5. If the train in Prob. 4 arrives at a 0.5 per cent up grade 1 mile long and the drawbar pull remains the same, with what velocity will it reach the end of the grade?   *Ans.* 35.2 mi. per hr.

6. If the system of bodies shown in Fig. 296 is released from rest, determine the velocity of the 60-lb. body after moving 10 ft. Compute the tension in the cord.   *Ans.* 9.95 ft. per sec.; 69.2 lb.

7. The speed of rotation of the flywheel of a punch press decreases from 180 r.p.m. to 150 r.p.m. as the machine punches a $\frac{1}{2}$-in. diameter hole through plate $\frac{1}{4}$ in. thick whose ultimate shearing strength is 60,000 lb. per sq. in. If 80 per cent of the energy lost by the flywheel is used in punching the hole, compute the required moment of inertia of the flywheel.   *Ans.* 5.64.

8. The energy of a 500-lb. load dropped from rest through a free distance of 15 in. is to be absorbed by a helical spring. If the allowable shortening of the spring is 3 in., compute the scale of the spring required.   *Ans.* 2000 lb. per in.

FIG. 296.

9. A 40-lb. block is projected along a horizontal surface by a 200-lb. spring whose initial deflection is 6 in. If the coefficient of friction is 0.2, what velocity will the block have after moving 20 ft.?

Ans. 15 ft. per sec.

10. What initial deflection must be given the spring of Prob. 9 in order that it may project the 40-lb. block upward to a height of 25 ft.?

Ans. 11 in

11. A rod 3 ft. long is attached to a horizontal axis normal to the rod through one end. If the rod is held at rest with its center vertically above the axis and then released, with what angular velocity will it pass through a position 120° farther on? *Ans.* 6.95 rad. per sec.

12. The rotating parts of the windlass shown in Fig. 297 weigh 200 lb. and have a radius of gyration of $1\frac{1}{4}$ ft. The 800-lb. load has downward velocity of 10 ft. per sec. just before the brake is applied. Compute the distance the load will travel in coming to rest if the coefficient of friction for the brake on the drum is 0.4, and friction of bearings is neglected. *Ans.* 14.1 ft.

Fig. 297.

13. A Prony brake (see Fig. 295) attached to a 4-ft. diameter flywheel has a lever arm of 5 ft. When the wheel is rotating at a speed of 300 r.p.m. the force P is observed to be 200 lb. Compute the horsepower being developed. *Ans.* 57.1 hp.

14. The velocity of the water in a penstock of 6-ft. diameter is 8 ft. per sec. Compute the horsepower available. *Ans.* 25.6 hp.

15. A belt is in contact with half the circumference of a 2-ft. diameter pulley which it is driving with a speed of 240 r.p.m. The coefficient of belt friction is 0.4. If the belt is transmitting 60 hp. and is on the point of slipping, compute the tension on each side. *Ans.* 1840 lb.; 522 lb.

CHAPTER XI

DYNAMICS OF ROTATING BODIES

Art. 79. The Effective Forces on a Rotating Body. If a rigid body is acted upon by forces causing the body to rotate about an

FIG. 298.

axis, each particle in the body will move in a plane circular path whose center is at the axis of rotation. Each particle will therefore have an acceleration which may be represented by its tangential and normal components. In Fig. 298 is shown a rigid body rotating with an angular velocity ω and angular acceleration α about an axis through 0. Let dM be the mass of any particle located at radial distance ρ from 0. The tangential component of the acceleration of the particle is $a_t = \rho\alpha$, and the normal component of the acceleration is $a_n = \rho\omega^2$. According to Newton's second law, the effective forces on the particle required to produce these acceleration components are $dM\rho\alpha$ tangent to the path, and $dM\rho\omega^2$ normal to the path and directed toward the center, as shown in Fig. 299. Each particle in the body is

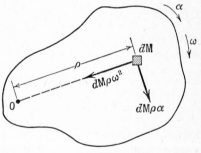

FIG. 299.

acted upon by a similar pair of effective forces. The resultant of these effective forces for the entire body and the moment of

196

the effective forces with respect to the axis of rotation enter into the analysis of many problems involving rotating bodies.

Art. 80. The Moment of the Effective Forces. The effective forces acting on the particles of a rotating body represent the effect of the external forces acting on the body. The sum of their moments with respect to the axis of rotation must therefore be equal to the sum of the moments of the external forces on the body with respect to the same axis. In Fig. 300, let F_1, F_2, F_3, etc., at distances r_1, r_2, r_3, etc., from O, represent the various external forces (including weight of the body and reactions at supports) acting on the rotating body. The sum of the moments of these external forces with respect to O is

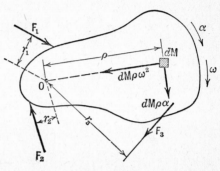

FIG. 300.

$$F_1 r_1 + F_2 r_2 + F_3 r_3 + \text{etc.} = \Sigma Fr$$

The moment of the effective forces on the particle of mass dM with respect to O is

$$dM\rho\omega^2 \times 0 + dM\rho\alpha \times \rho = dM\rho^2\alpha$$

The sum of the moments of the effective forces for the entire body is $\int dM\rho^2\alpha$. Since all particles in the body have the angular acceleration α in common, the moment of the effective forces becomes

$$\alpha \int \rho^2 dM = I_0 \alpha$$

where $I_0 = \int \rho^2 dM$ is the moment of inertia of the mass of the body with respect to the axis of rotation. Equating the moment of the external forces to the moment of the effective forces,

$$\Sigma Fr = I_0 \alpha$$

This equation for rotation is analogous to the equation $F = Ma$ for rectilinear motion.

Example

The rotating parts of the windlass, shown in Fig. 301 (a), weigh 300 lb. and have a radius of gyration of 2 ft. The coefficient of friction

FIG. 301.

for the brake is 0.4 and bearing friction is assumed to be negligible. Determine the angular acceleration of the windlass and the tension in the cable.

Solution: The windlass and load are shown separately as free bodies in Fig. 301 (b). It may be determined by inspection that the brake friction is not sufficient to hold the load and therefore the load will accelerate downward. For the windlass,

$$I_0 = \frac{W}{g} k^2 = \frac{300}{32.2} (2)^2 = 37.3$$

By substitution in the equation $\Sigma Fr = I\alpha$,

$$T \times 2 - 0.4 \times 600 \times 3 = 37.3\alpha \qquad (1)$$

By $\Sigma F_v = 0$ for the load,

$$T + \frac{500 \, a_t}{32.2} = 500 \qquad (2)$$

Also,

$$a_t = r\alpha = 2\alpha \qquad (3)$$

By simultaneous solution of equations (1) to (3),

$$T = 413 \text{ lb.}; \; \alpha = 2.82 \text{ rad. per sec.}^2$$

A variation in the solution may be had by considering the entire system as a single free body as shown in Fig. 302.   The equation $\Sigma Fr = I_0\alpha$ applied to the entire system becomes

$$500 \times 2 - \frac{500}{32.2} \times 2\alpha \times 2 - 0.4 \times 600 \times 3 = 37.3\alpha$$

$$\alpha = 2.82 \text{ rad. per sec.}^2$$

Then, using the 500-lb. load as a free body,

$$T + \frac{500 \ (2 \times 2.82)}{32.2} = 500$$

$$T = 413 \text{ lb.}$$

FIG. 302.

Problems

1. A cast-iron cylinder 1 ft. in diameter and 2 ft. long is mounted on a shaft through its geometric axis.   A 50-lb. weight is suspended from a cord wrapped around the cylinder.   Neglecting journal friction, compute the linear acceleration of the weight and the tension in the cord.
    Ans. 4 ft. per sec. per sec.; 43.8 lb.

2. Solve Prob. 1 if the shaft on which the cylinder rotates has a 2-in. diameter and the coefficient of journal friction is 0.05.
    Ans. 3.49 ft. per sec. per sec.; 44.6 lb.

3. The rotating portion of the system shown in Fig. 303 weighs 150 lb. and has a radius of gyration of 1.5 ft.   If the coefficient of friction for the

FIG. 303.   FIG. 304.

100-lb. block is 0.3, determine its acceleration and the tension in the attached cable.   *Ans.* 9.63 ft. per sec. per sec.; 59.9 lb.

4. The rotating parts of the windlass shown in Fig. 304 weigh 300 lb. and

have a radius of gyration of 1.25 ft.   The coefficient of friction for the brake
is 0.4 and axle friction is negligible.   If the 600-lb. load has a downward
velocity of 20 ft. per sec. just before the brake is applied, how far will it travel
in coming to rest?   *Ans.* 32 ft.

   5. A flywheel weighing 600 lb. has a radius of gyration of 1.75 ft.   A
1500-lb. load is suspended from a cable wrapped around a pulley of 1-ft.
diameter fastened to the flywheel.   The load is being raised with a velocity
of 15 ft. per sec. just before the power is cut off.   If bearing friction is neglected,
how much farther will the load continue to rise and what will be the tension
in the cable while the system comes to rest?   *Ans.* 20.6 ft.; 1250 lb.

   6. Solve the Example of Art. 77 using the method of this article.

Art. 81. The Resultant of the Effective Forces.

It was shown
in Art. 79 that each particle of a rigid rotating body is acted upon
by an effective force whose components are $dM\rho\alpha$ acting tangent
to the path in the direction of the angular acceleration, and
$dM\rho\omega^2$ acting radially toward the axis of rotation.   The tangential
and normal components of the resultant of these forces for the
entire body will now be determined for a body possessing a plane
of symmetry normal to the axis of rotation.   A body satisfying
this requirement may be considered as composed of elementary
rods normal to the plane of symmetry.   The resultant effective
forces on each rod will act at its midpoint and thus lie in the plane
of symmetry, forming a
coplanar system in the
plane of motion of the
center of gravity of the
body.

   In Fig. 305 is shown
the plane of symmetry
of such a rotating body
as described.   As before,
dM represents a particle
located at radial distance
ρ from the axis of rotation through O and acted
upon by the tangential

FIG. 305.

and normal components of the effective force. C represents the
center of gravity of the body and $\bar{r}$ its radial distance from the
axis of rotation.   Let N and T be rectangular axes selected so that
N passes through the center of gravity and axis of rotation.   Let
θ be the angle between the radius ρ and the N axis.

The summation of the components of the effective forces parallel to the N axis is

$$\Sigma F_N = \int dM \rho \alpha \sin \theta - \int dM \rho \omega^2 \cos \theta$$

Since $\rho \sin \theta = y$, $\rho \cos \theta = x$, and α and ω^2 are common to all particles,

$$\Sigma F_N = \alpha \int y \, dM - \omega^2 \int x \, dM = M \bar{y} \alpha - M \bar{x} \omega^2$$

However, since y is measured from the N axis which was taken through the center of gravity, $\bar{y} = 0$ and $M \bar{y} \alpha = 0$. Also, since x is measured from the T axis and the distance of the center of gravity from that axis was originally denoted by $\bar{r}$, $\bar{x} = \bar{r}$. Thus, the resultant of all effective forces on the body has a component in the N or normal direction given by

$$\mathbf{\Sigma F_N = M \, \bar{r} \, \omega^2}$$

Referring again to Fig. 305, the summation of the components of the effective forces parallel to the T axis is

$$\Sigma F_T = \int dM \rho \alpha \cos \theta + \int dM \, \rho \omega^2 \sin \theta$$

$$= \alpha \int x \, dM + \omega^2 \int y \, dM$$

$$= M \bar{x} \alpha + M \bar{y} \omega^2$$

Since $\bar{x} = \bar{r}$ and $\bar{y} = 0$ as already explained,

$$\mathbf{\Sigma F_T = M \, \bar{r} \, \alpha}$$

The resultant effective force for the rotating body may now be expressed in terms of its components $M \bar{r} \omega^2$ in the N direction and $M \bar{r} \alpha$ in the T direction. The positions of these components will next be determined. The components of a force may be considered as acting together at any point on the line of action of the force; it will be convenient in this development and subsequent applications to have the components $M \bar{r} \omega^2$ and $M \bar{r} \alpha$ act at the point where their resultant intersects the N axis. The $M \bar{r} \omega^2$ component will then lie along the N axis; that is, it acts radially along the line joining the axis of rotation and center of gravity.

The $M\bar{r}\alpha$ component will be perpendicular to the N axis at some distance q from the axis of rotation. The distance q may be found by equating the sum of the moments of the resultant forces $M\bar{r}\omega^2$ and $M\bar{r}\alpha$ with respect to the axis of rotation to the sum of the moments of the effective forces acting on the elementary particles. The sum of the moments of the elementary effective forces was shown in Art. 80 to be $I_0\alpha$. Hence

$$M\bar{r}\omega^2 \cdot 0 + M\bar{r}\alpha \cdot q = I_0\alpha = Mk_0^2\alpha$$

$$q = \frac{I_0}{M\bar{r}} = \frac{k_0^2}{\bar{r}}$$

The preceding discussion may now be summarized in the following statements:

1. The resultant normal effective force is $M\bar{r}\omega^2$ acting radially through the center of gravity toward the axis of rotation.

FIG. 306.

2. The resultant tangential effective force is $M\bar{r}\alpha$ acting perpendicular to the line through the center of gravity and axis of rotation at a distance $k_0^2/\bar{r}$ from the axis of rotation.

The above results are illustrated by Fig. 306 (a) which shows the resultant normal and tangential effective forces for the entire body. In the solution of problems in rotation by means of D'Alembert's principle (see Art. 62), these forces are reversed in direction and applied to the free body as shown in Fig. 306 (*b*). They are now known as the reversed normal and tangential effective forces or the inertia forces for the rotating body. The normal reversed effective force $M\bar{r}\omega^2$ is often called the centrifugal force. The addition of the reversed effective forces to the system of forces actually acting on the rotating body forms a system of forces in equilibrium, thus reducing the problem to one of static equilibrium.

It is evident from the expressions $M\bar{r}\omega^2$ and $M\bar{r}\alpha$ that both forces reduce to zero when the axis of rotation passes through the center of gravity ($\bar{r} = 0$). It is also evident that $M\bar{r}\alpha$ is zero when the speed of rotation is constant ($\alpha = 0$). The force $M\bar{r}\omega^2$ increases in proportion to the square of the angular speed.

The results obtained above were derived for the special case of a body possessing a plane of symmetry normal to the axis of rotation. It can be shown that these results are also valid for a body possessing a line of symmetry parallel to the axis of rotation. In the general case of rotating bodies, however, the resultant effective forces do not necessarily lie in the plane of rotation of the center of gravity and their exact position is usually difficult to determine. Most problems of rotation in engineering come under the special cases just described. One important exception, a slender rod inclined at any angle to its axis of rotation, is considered later. (See Prob. 4 to follow.)

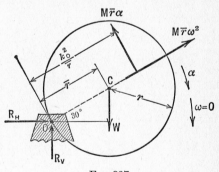

FIG. 307.

Example 1

A circular disk of radius *r* and weight *W* is attached to a horizontal axis through an element of the cylindrical surface. If the disk is held at rest with its center at 30° above the horizontal and then released and allowed to rotate under the influence of gravity alone, determine completely the reversed effective forces for the disk at the instant of release.

Solution: In Fig. 307 the disk is shown as a free body at the instant of release. In this position, it is acted upon by its weight and the reaction components R_V and R_H at the axis of rotation. The reversed effective forces are shown in their proper positions according to the requirements determined above.

Since the angular velocity ω is zero at the instant of release,

$$M\bar{r}\omega^2 = 0$$

The angular acceleration for this position is found by means of the equation

$$\Sigma Fr = I_0\alpha$$

$$I_0 = \tfrac{3}{2}Mr^2 \text{ by transfer from } C$$

$$W \times \bar{r} \cos 30° = \frac{3}{2}\frac{W}{g}r^2\alpha$$

$$\alpha = \frac{2}{3}\frac{g}{r}\cos 30°$$

$$M\bar{r}\alpha = \frac{W}{g}\cdot r\cdot\frac{2}{3}\frac{g}{r}\cos 30° = \frac{2}{3}W\cos 30° = 0.577W$$

$$\frac{k_0{}^2}{\bar{r}} = \frac{I_0}{M\bar{r}} = \frac{\tfrac{3}{2}M\bar{r}^2}{M\bar{r}} = \frac{3}{2}r$$

The magnitude of the force $M\bar{r}\alpha$ may also be determined by an alternative method in which the distance $k_0{}^2/\bar{r}$ is first computed and then the equation $\Sigma M_0 = 0$ gives

$$M\bar{r}\alpha \times \tfrac{3}{2}r - W \times r \cos 30° = 0$$

$$M\bar{r}\alpha = \tfrac{2}{3}W \cos 30° = 0.577\ W$$

Example 2

If the diameter of the disk in Ex. 1 is 1 ft. and its weight is 50 lb., determine completely the reversed effective forces when it is rotated at a constant speed of 150 r.p.m. about the same axis.

Solution: Since the angular acceleration α is zero when the speed of rotation is constant,

$$M\bar{r}\alpha = 0$$

$$M\bar{r}\omega^2 = \frac{50}{32.2} \times \frac{1}{2} \times \left[\frac{150}{60} \times 2\pi\right]^2 = 192 \text{ lb.}$$

Problems

1. Solve Ex. 1 if the center C is horizontally opposite the axis of rotation at the instant of release. $\qquad$ *Ans.* $M\bar{r}\alpha = \frac{2}{3}W$.

2. Solve Prob. 1 if the axis of rotation passes through the disk midway between the center and the outside edge.

$$Ans.\ M\bar{r}\alpha = \tfrac{1}{3}W;\ k_0^2/\bar{r} = \tfrac{3}{2}r.$$

3. A flywheel weighing 2000 lb. rotates at 300 r.p.m. about an axis which is 0.05 in. off center. Compute the normal reversed effective force.

Ans. 255 lb.

4. Show that the resultant normal effective force for a slender prismatic rod rotating about a vertical axis through one end is $M\bar{r}\omega^2$ and acts radially through a point in the rod at two-thirds the length from the point of support.

5. A steel rod 1 in. in diameter and 30 in. long is fastened to a vertical axis through one end so that the rod is inclined at 30° with the vertical. Compute the normal effective force for the rod when its speed of rotation is 60 r.p.m. $\qquad$ *Ans.* 5.13 lb.

Art. 82. Kinetic Reactions. If the resultant normal and tangential effective forces for a rotating body are zero, the reactions at the supports of the body are the same as when the body is at rest. If, however, the nature of the rotating body is such that either one or both of the effective forces is not zero, additional components will be introduced into the reactions at the supports. Furthermore, these additional components of the reactions vary in both magnitude and direction as the position of the rotating body and its speed of rotation change. Those components of the reactions at the supports of a rotating body which vary in magnitude and direction as the body rotates are known as the *kinetic components*, whereas those components which remain constant are known as the *static components*. In order to determine the reactions at the supports of a rotating body, the free-body diagram is drawn, including both known and unknown forces acting upon the body, the normal and tangential effective forces are determined and added in the reversed direction, after which the necessary equations of static equilibrium are applied to complete the solution.

Example 1

A slender prismatic rod, 6 ft. long and weighing 50 lb., is held at rest in a vertical position with its center directly above a horizontal axis through the lower end. If the rod is released from this position and allowed to rotate under the influence of gravity alone, determine the normal and tangential components of the reaction at the support as the rod passes through a position 30° below the horizontal.

Solution: The free-body diagram of the rod as it rotates through the designated position is shown in Fig. 308.

$$I_0 = \frac{1}{3}\frac{W}{g}l^2 = \frac{1}{3}\frac{50}{32.2}(6)^2 = 18.6$$

$$k_0{}^2 = \tfrac{1}{3}l^2 = \tfrac{1}{3}(6)^2 = 12$$

$$\frac{k_0{}^2}{\bar{r}} = \frac{12}{3} = 4 \text{ ft.}$$

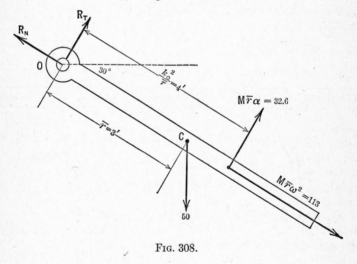

FIG. 308.

The angular acceleration α is determined by applying $\Sigma Fr = I_0\alpha$,

$$50 \times 3 \cos 30° = 18.6\alpha$$

$$\alpha = 7.00 \text{ rad. per sec.}^2$$

$$M\bar{r}\alpha = \frac{50}{32.2} \times 3 \times 7 = 32.6 \text{ lb.}$$

$M\bar{r}\alpha$ may also be determined by applying $\Sigma M_0 = 0$,

$$M\bar{r}\alpha \times 4 - 50 \times 3 \cos 30° = 0$$

$$M\bar{r}\alpha = 32.6 \text{ lb.}$$

The angular velocity ω is found by equating the work of gravity to the increase in kinetic energy, or $W\bar{h} = \frac{1}{2}I_0\omega^2$. The center of gravity of the rod has been lowered a total distance $\bar{h} = 4.5$ ft. from its initial position; and so

$$50 \times 4.5 = \tfrac{1}{2} \times 18.6\omega^2$$

$$\omega^2 = 24.2$$

$$M\bar{r}\omega^2 = 113 \text{ lb.}$$

If the reversed effective forces as computed are applied to the free body, it will be in a state of static equilibrium and the normal and tangential components, R_N and R_T, of the reaction at O, may be determined. In Fig. 308,

$$\Sigma F_N = R_N - 113 - 50 \sin 30° = 0 \qquad R_N = 138 \text{ lb.}$$

$$\Sigma F_T = R_T + 32.6 - 50 \cos 30° = 0 \qquad R_T = 10.7 \text{ lb.}$$

Example 2

The rod of Ex. 1 rotates with constant speed of 30 r.p.m. about a vertical axis through one end. Determine the angle at which the rod will stand out from the axis, and the vertical and horizontal components of the reaction at the support.

Solution: The free-body diagram of the rod is shown in Fig. 309. Since the speed of rotation is constant, $\alpha = 0$, and $M\bar{r}\alpha = 0$. Since the normal effective forces on the particles of this rotating body constitute a series of parallel forces acting radially through the axis of rotation and increasing in magnitude in proportion to the distances of the consecutive particles from the axis, their resultant will be $M\bar{r}\omega^2$, acting through point Q

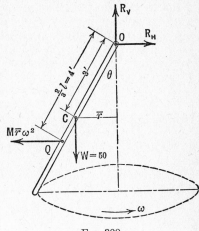

Fig. 309.

at two-thirds the length of the rod from the support O. (See Prob. 4, Art. 81.) If this force is reversed in direction and applied to the free body as shown, the system is in equilibrium, and the equation $\Sigma M_O = 0$ gives

$$\frac{W}{g}\,\bar{r}\omega^2 \cdot \frac{2}{3}\,l\cos\theta - W\bar{r} = 0$$

$$\cos \theta = \frac{3g}{2\omega^2 l} = \frac{3 \times 32.2}{2(\frac{30}{60} \times 2\pi)^2 \times 6} = 0.815$$

$$\theta = 35.4°$$

$$\bar{r} = 3 \sin \theta = 1.73 \text{ ft.}$$

$$M\bar{r}\omega^2 = \frac{50}{32.2} \times 1.73 \times \pi^2 = 26.5 \text{ lb.}$$

$$\Sigma F_V = R_V - 50 = 0 \qquad R_V = 50 \text{ lb.}$$

$$\Sigma F_H = R_H - 26.5 = 0 \qquad R_H = 26.5 \text{ lb.}$$

Problems

1. Solve for the vertical and horizontal components of the reaction of the support in Ex. 1 as the rod passes through the horizontal position.
Ans. R_V = 12.5 lb.; R_H = 75.0 lb.

2. Solve for the vertical and horizontal components of the reaction of the support in Ex. 1 as the rod passes through the vertical position with its center directly below the axis.   *Ans.* R_V = 200 lb.; R_H = 0.

3. Solve for the speed of rotation required to make the rod in Ex. 2 stand at 60° with the vertical axis.   *Ans.* 38.3 r.p.m.

4. A cast-iron sphere 6 in. in diameter is connected by a stiff rod to a horizontal axis 2 ft. from the center of the sphere. If the sphere is released from rest with its center vertically above the axis and allowed to rotate under the influence of gravity alone, compute the vertical and horizontal components of the reaction at the support when the angular displacement of the system is 60°. Neglect the weight of the arm.   *Ans.* R_V = 7.13 lb.; R_H = 12.7 lb.

5. A 500-lb. flywheel rotates at 1800 r.p.m. about a horizontal axis 1/16 in. off center. If the wheel is midway between bearings, compute the maximum and minimum values of the bearing reactions.

Ans. 1690 lb.; −1190 lb.

6. A cast-iron disk of 20-in. diameter and 2-in. thickness rotates at 100 r.p.m. about a vertical axis AB through an element of its curved surface as shown in Fig. 310. Determine the x and y components of the reactions at the bearings A and B.

Ans. A_x = 110 lb.; A_y = 163 lb.;
B_x = 354 lb.; B_y = 0.

Fig. 310.

7. A steel rod, 2 in. in diameter and 8 ft. long, is released from rest in a horizontal position and allowed to rotate, under the influence of gravity alone, about a horizontal axis normal to the rod through a point

2 ft. from its end.   Compute the vertical and horizontal components of the reaction at the support as the rod passes through a position 60° below the horizontal.   *Ans.* $R_V = 131$ lb.; $R_H = 47.5$ lb.

Art. 83. Balancing of Rotating Bodies.   It was shown in Art. 82 that the reactions at the supports of rotating bodies often include kinetic components which vary in magnitude and direction as the body rotates.   As a result of these kinetic reactions injurious effects such as vibration and undue wear of bearings may occur. It is therefore desirable to eliminate such reactions.   Balancing may be defined as the addition or removal of such rotating parts as will cause the effective forces for the entire system to be in equilibrium and thus induce no kinetic reactions.

A rotating body may be in static balance or dynamic balance. If a body has no tendency to rotate regardless of the position in which it is placed, it is said to be in *static balance*.   If no kinetic reactions are induced when the body rotates, it is said to be in *dynamic balance*.   It is possible for a body to be statically balanced and yet not dynamically balanced.   The crank shaft of a two-cylinder engine, shown in Fig. 311, serves as an example.   If the two eccentric portions are identical, the shaft will not rotate when placed in frictionless bearings at A and B, regardless of its position,

FIG. 311.

and is therefore in static balance.   However, when the shaft rotates, it exerts upon the bearings a centrifugal couple composed of the forces $M_1\bar{r}_1\omega^2$ and $M_2\bar{r}_2\omega^2$, and kinetic reactions are induced at A and B.   The shaft is thus not in dynamic balance.   It is necessary to add counterweights to the shaft to balance it completely.

The following discussion will be limited to rotation at constant speed, so that only normal effective forces need be considered.

Art. 84. Balancing in a Single Transverse Plane.   If a rotating system contains a part, of weight W_1, at radial distance $\bar{r}_1$ from the axis of rotation, exerting a centrifugal pull $\dfrac{W_1}{g}\,\bar{r}_1\omega^2$, balancing may be accomplished by addition of another part, of weight W_2, placed diametrically opposite in the same plane of rotation and at such distance r_2 from the axis that

$$\frac{W_1}{g}\,\bar{r}_1\omega^2 = \frac{W_2}{g}\,\bar{r}_2\omega^2$$

The balanced system is shown in Fig. 312. Since g and ω are common factors, the above requirement for balance may be expressed as

$$W_1\bar{r}_1 = W_2\,\bar{r}_2$$

This is also the requirement for static balance. In practice, dynamic balance, for rotating bodies in which the bulk of the ma-

terial lies approximately in a single plane of rotation, may be accomplished by adding or removing material until static balance is obtained.

If the rotating system contains several unbalanced parts in the same transverse plane, each part may be individually balanced by adding a balancing weight diametrically oppo-

Fig. 312.

site in the same plane, thus introducing as many balancing weights as there are unbalanced parts. However, since it has previously been shown that the balancing operation reduces to one of balancing forces, and since the system of forces is concurrent, it is evident that only one balancing weight W, so placed that its centrifugal pull $\frac{W}{g}\,\bar{r}\omega^2$ will hold in equilibrium the centrifugal pulls of the parts to be balanced, will be sufficient. As previously pointed out, the $W\bar{r}$ products may be used instead of the actual forces. The required balancing weight and its position may be determined graphically by means of the vector polygon of the $W\bar{r}$ products, or algebraically by summation of the $W\bar{r}$ products in each of two directions. Either W or $\bar{r}$ for the balancing weight may be assumed and the other computed.

Example 1

The system of three rotating bodies shown in Fig. 313 is to be balanced by a weight W at 12 in. from the axis of rotation. Determine W and the angle θ at which it must be placed.

Solution: The summation of $W\bar{r}$ products in the x direction gives

$$W \times 12 \cos \theta + 20 \times 10 \sin 60° - 50 \times 6 = 0$$

$$W \cos \theta = 10.6 \tag{1}$$

The summation of $W\bar{r}$ products in the y direction gives

$$20 \times 10 \sin 30° + 10 \times 8 - W \times 12 \sin \theta = 0$$

$$W \sin \theta = 15.0 \tag{2}$$

Simultaneous solution of equations (1) and (2) gives

$$W = 18.4 \text{ lb.}; \quad \theta = 54.7°$$

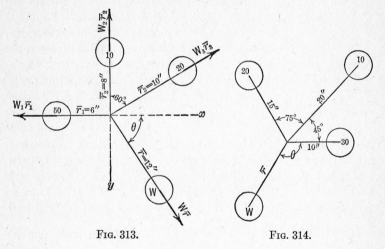

FIG. 313.   FIG. 314.

Problems

1. In Fig. 313, let $W_1 = 60$ lb., $\bar{r}_1 = 8$ in., $W_2 = 0$, $W_3 = 45$ lb., and $\bar{r}_3 = 6$ in. If $\bar{r} = 10$ in., determine W and θ.

Ans. $W = 28$ lb.; $\theta = 28.8°$.

2. A steel disk 2 ft. in diameter and 1 in. thick rotates about an axis 1/16 in. from its geometric axis. At what distance from the axis of rotation should a 2-in. diameter hole be drilled to balance the disk?   Ans. 9 in.

3. If the balancing weight W for the system shown in Fig. 314 is to be 40 lb., determine $\bar{r}$ and θ.

Ans. 12.4 in.; 126°.

Art. 85. Balancing in Different Transverse Planes. The balancing weight for a rotating body cannot always be placed in the plane of rotation of the body. The crankshaft of Fig. 311 is an example of this situation. When the balancing weight cannot be

placed in the same transverse plane as the rotating body, balancing can be accomplished by the addition of two balancing weights in different planes normal to the axis. Thus, in Fig. 315, the weight W_1 at distance r_1 from the axis AB may be balanced by addition of weights W_A and W_B in the same axial plane but in different transverse planes through A and B and at distances l_A and l_B from the plane of weight W_1.

Fig. 315.

The necessary conditions for balance are obtained from the equations:

$$\Sigma M_A = W_1 \bar{r}_1 l_A - W_B \bar{r}_B l = 0$$

$$\Sigma M_B = W_1 \bar{r}_1 l_B - W_A \bar{r}_A l = 0$$

If the same shaft carries additional unbalanced parts W_2, W_3, etc., each of the additional parts can be balanced by the addition of a balancing weight in plane A and one in plane B. Finally, all the balancing weights in the transverse plane A can be replaced by a single weight, and those in the transverse plane B can likewise be replaced by a single weight.

Example

The rotating system shown in Fig. 316 is to be balanced by the addition of a weight W_A to be placed in the normal plane at A and a weight W_E to be placed in the normal plane at E, each at 6 in. from the axis of rotation. Determine the required values of W_A and W_E and their angular positions.

Solution: The system is projected into coordinate planes as shown in Fig. 317. The true values of the $W\bar{r}$ products are shown in Fig. 317 (c).

The projected values of these products are given in Fig. 317 (a) and (b).

FIG. 316.

In the projected system of Fig. 317 (a), the equation $\Sigma M_A = 0$ gives

$$(W_E \bar{r}_E)_H \times 4 = 200 \times 3 + 240 \times 2 - 500 \times 1$$

$$(W_E \bar{r}_E)_H = 145$$

Similarly, from the equation $\Sigma M_E = 0$,

$$(W_A \bar{r}_A)_H = 205$$

FIG. 317.

In the projected system of Fig. 317 (b), the equations $\Sigma M_A = 0$ and $\Sigma M_E = 0$ give

$$(W_E \bar{r}_E)_V = 52.0$$

$$(W_A \bar{r}_A)_V = 122$$

The $W\bar{r}$ components in plane A are shown in Fig. 318 (a), and those for plane E in Fig. 318 (b). By combination of the components in plane A,

$$W_A\bar{r}_A = \sqrt{(205)^2 + (122)^2} = 238$$

$$W_A = \frac{238}{6} = 39.7 \text{ lb.}$$

$$\theta_A = \tan^{-1}\frac{122}{205} = 30.8°$$

(a) (b)

FIG. 318.

By combination of the components in plane E,

$$W_E\bar{r}_E = \sqrt{(52)^2 + (145)^2} = 154$$

$$W_E = \frac{154}{6} = 25.7 \text{ lb.}$$

$$\theta_E = \tan^{-1}\frac{52}{145} = 19.7°$$

Problems

1. The crank shaft of a single-cylinder gas engine is 3 ft. long between bearings. The plane of rotation of the crank is 1 ft. from the left bearing. The crank arms and pin are equivalent to a weight of 60 lb. at a radial distance of 8 in. from the axis of rotation. The crank is to be balanced by weights at 6-in. radial distance in each of two planes 6 in. from the bearings. Determine the balancing weights required. *Ans.* 60 lb. at left; 20 lb. at right.

2. A two-cylinder engine has a crank shaft like the one described in Prob. 1 except that a second crank, similar to the first, rotates in a plane at 1 ft. from the right bearing and 180° back of the first crank. Determine the balancing weights to be placed in the same normal planes and at the same radial distance as before. *Ans.* 40 lb. at left; 40 lb. at right.

FIG. 319.

3. The rotating system shown in Fig. 319 is to be balanced by a weight at 5 in. from the axis of rotation in the normal plane A and a weight at 3 in.

from the axis in the normal plane B. Determine the balancing weights required and their location in their respective planes.

Ans. $W_A = 103$ lb.; $\theta = 248°$; $W_B = 259$ lb.; $\theta = 189°$.

Art. 86. Circumferential Tension in Flywheels.

When a fly-wheel rotates, the centrifugal action exerted on the rim causes a circumferential or " hoop " tension to be developed in the rim. This stress increases as the square of the velocity, as will be shown, and may become quite important at high speeds. If the tension in the spokes is neglected, the tension in the rim may be determined.

In Fig. 320 is shown the half of the rim of a flywheel. If the thickness of the rim is small compared to the mean radius r, the center of gravity C of the half-rim coincides very nearly with the centroid of the semicircular arc of radius r. Thus, $\bar{r} = 2r/\pi$.

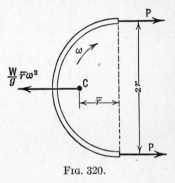

FIG. 320.

Now, if W represents the weight of the half-rim, the normal reversed effective force becomes

$$\frac{W}{g}\bar{r}\omega^2 = \frac{2Wr\omega^2}{\pi g}$$

This force is in equilibrium with the induced tensile forces P, P in the rim. Thus,

$$2P = \frac{2Wr\omega^2}{\pi g} \quad \text{or} \quad P = \frac{Wr\omega^2}{\pi g}$$

The unit stress S in the rim is P/A, so

$$S = \frac{Wr\omega^2}{\pi g A}$$

Since $W = \pi r A\gamma$, where $\gamma =$ weight per unit volume,

$$S = \frac{r^2\omega^2\gamma}{g} = \frac{\gamma v^2}{g} \approx ML^{-1}T^{-2}$$

When γ is in pounds per cubic foot, v in feet per second, and g in feet per second per second, S will be in pounds per square foot.

Problems

1. A cast-iron flywheel 6 ft. in diameter outside has a rim 4 in. thick. Compute the unit tensile stress in the rim when the speed of rotation is 300 r.p.m. Neglect the tension in the spokes.   *Ans.* 770 lb. per sq. in.

2. If the allowable tensile stress for cast iron is 3000 lb. per sq. in., compute the maximum safe speed in revolutions per minute for a cast-iron flywheel of 12-ft. outside diameter and 2-in. rim thickness.   *Ans.* 284 r.p.m.

3. The two halves of a 2500-lb. flywheel are cast separately and then fastened together by 6 rivets of 1-in. diameter each. If the mean diameter of the rim is 10 ft. and the wheel rotates at 180 r.p.m., compute the unit tensile stress in the rivets.   *Ans.* 9320 lb. per sq. in.

Art. 87. The Loaded Conical Pendulum Governor. It was shown in Art. 65 that the height h of a conical pendulum depends

only on the angular speed and is not affected by the weight of the rotating mass or the length of its arm. By means of a suitable mechanism the change in height of the pendulum due to a variation in speed may be made to actuate a valve and thereby control the speed of the engine by which it is being rotated. Such a device, known as a simple conical pendulum governor, is shown in Fig. 321.

FIG. 321.

It may be seen that in this type of governor the change in height h for a given change in speed is greater at low speed than at high speed. In order to make the governor more sensitive at high speed, the height h may be increased by loading. In Fig. 322 (*a*) is shown such a loaded governor.

The load W_1 on the governor is shown as a free body in Fig. 322 (*b*). Equation $\Sigma F_v = 0$ gives

$$T = \frac{W_1}{2 \cos \phi}$$

One of the rotating spheres is shown as a free body in Fig. 322 (*c*). Since the weight of the arm is usually small compared to the

weight of the sphere it may be neglected without appreciable error.
The equation $\Sigma M_C = 0$ gives

$$W \cdot \bar{r} + T \cdot d = \frac{W}{g} \bar{r} \omega^2 \cdot h$$

FIG. 322.

The relations between the weights involved, the angles, and speed
of rotation may be determined from the two equations above.

Problems

1. If $AB = 6$ in., $BC = 12$ in., $W = 30$ lb., $W_1 = 150$ lb., and $\theta = \phi = 45°$
for the governor of Fig. 322 when it is at rest, at what speed will it begin to
act?   *Ans.* 302 r.p.m.

2. What load W_1 on the governor of Prob. 1 will cause it to begin to act
at a speed of 200 r.p.m.?   *Ans.* 57.2 lb.

Art. 88. Center of Percussion. If an
impulsive force or blow F is applied to a
body suspended from an axis O, as shown
in Fig. 323, an angular acceleration will
result. As shown in Art. 81, the resultant
tangential effective force $M\bar{r}\alpha$ acts at point
Q, at distance $k_0^2/\bar{r}$ from the axis O. With
this force applied in the reversed direction,
the body is in equilibrium. From the equation $\Sigma M_Q = 0$, it is seen that a tangential
reaction R_x will be induced at O whose
direction is to the left when the blow F is
struck above Q and to the right when the
blow is struck below Q. It is evident that,
if the blow were struck at Q, the tangential
reaction R_x must be zero regardless of the magnitude of force F.

FIG. 323.

The point Q, at which the body may be struck without producing a tangential reaction at the support, is called the *center of percussion*.

Problems

1. A uniform slender rod 6 ft. long is suspended from a horizontal axis passing through the rod at 1 ft. from the end. Locate the center of percussion with respect to the lower end of the rod. If a force of 20 lb. is applied horizontally at the center of gravity of the rod, determine the tangential reaction at the support. *Ans.* 1.5 ft.; 8.57 lb.

2. A cylindrical disk of 3-ft. diameter is suspended from a horizontal axis parallel to its geometric axis and 1 ft. from it. If a 50-lb. horizontal force is applied to the disk at the center, what tangential reaction at the support will result? *Ans.* 26.4 lb.

Fig. 324.

Art. 89. Compound Pendulum.

Any rigid body free to rotate under the influence of gravity about a horizontal axis not passing through the center of gravity is called a *compound pendulum*. In Fig. 324 is shown a compound pendulum, suspended from an axis through O, and having center of gravity at C. With the reversed effective forces added as shown, the body is in equilibrium, and the equation $\Sigma M_0 = 0$ gives

$$W \cdot \bar{r} \sin \theta = \frac{W}{g} \bar{r} \alpha \cdot \frac{k_0^2}{\bar{r}}$$

$$\alpha = \frac{\bar{r}}{k_0^2} g \sin \theta$$

The tangential acceleration of point Q is

$$a_t = r\alpha = \frac{k_0^2}{\bar{r}} \times \frac{\bar{r}}{k_0^2} g \sin \theta = g \sin \theta$$

This is identical with the acceleration of a simple circular pendulum as shown in Art. 67. Therefore the compound pendulum has the same motion as a simple circular pendulum whose length l equals the distance $k_0^2/\bar{r}$, and will oscillate with the same period.

Since the period of the simple pendulum has been shown to be

$$T = 2\pi \sqrt{\frac{l}{g}}$$

the period of the compound pendulum becomes

$$T = 2\pi \sqrt{\frac{k_0{}^2}{g\bar{r}}}$$

The distance $k_0{}^2/\bar{r}$ is called the length of the compound pendulum and the point Q is called the *center of oscillation*. By referring to Art. 88, it is seen that the center of oscillation coincides with the center of percussion.

It may further be shown that the center of oscillation and point of suspension are interchangeable. In Fig. 324

$$CQ = \frac{k_0{}^2}{\bar{r}} - \bar{r}$$

Since

$$k_0{}^2 = k_C{}^2 + \bar{r}^2$$

$$CQ = \frac{k_C{}^2 + \bar{r}^2}{\bar{r}} - \bar{r} = \frac{k_C{}^2}{\bar{r}}$$

Now let Q be made the point of suspension. The new center of oscillation O' will be at distance CO' from the center of gravity. By analogy from the preceding equation

$$CO' = k_C{}^2/\bar{r}$$

The new $\bar{r}$ will now be the distance CQ. Thus

$$CO' = \frac{k_C{}^2}{CQ} = \frac{k_C{}^2}{\dfrac{k_C{}^2}{\bar{r}}} = \bar{r}$$

Therefore, O' must coincide with O, and what was formerly the point of suspension is now the center of oscillation.

The moment of inertia of a body of irregular shape which might be difficult, if not impossible, to compute, may be found experimentally by suspending the body from a horizontal axis and allowing it to oscillate as a compound pendulum. From the equation for the period of a compound pendulum, as stated above,

$$k_0{}^2 = \frac{T^2}{4\pi^2}\, g\bar{r}$$

$$I_0 = \frac{W}{g}\, k_0{}^2 = \frac{WT^2\bar{r}}{4\pi^2}$$

T may be found by observation of the period of oscillation, and $\bar{r}$ may be found by balancing. The moment of inertia I_0 with respect to the axis of suspension may then be computed.

Problems

1. A slender rod 3 ft. long is suspended from a horizontal axis through one end. Compute the period of oscillation. At what distance from the end may it be suspended and still have the same period? *Ans.* 1.56 sec.; 1 ft.

2. Determine the length of a slender rod which, when suspended from an axis through one end, will have a period of oscillation of 2 sec.

Ans. 4.89 ft.

3. A compound pendulum consists of a circular steel disk of 12-in. diameter and 1 in. thickness at the end of a steel rod 36 in. long, 4 in. wide, and 1 in. thick, suspended from a horizontal axis through its end, as shown in Fig. 325. Compute the period of oscillation. *Ans.* 1.91 sec.

ⁱ Fɪɢ. 325. Fɪɢ. 326.

4. The gear sector shown in Fig. 326 weighs 180 lb., and the distance of the center of gravity from the axis O is found by balancing to be 21 in. When allowed to oscillate as a compound pendulum about a horizontal axis through O, it is observed to make 40 complete oscillations per minute. Compute the moment of inertia of the gear sector with respect to its axis of rotation.

Ans. 17.9

Art. 90. Torsion Pendulum.

A body suspended by an elastic wire or slender rod and allowed to oscillate about the axis of the wire, as shown in Fig. 327, is known as a *torsion pendulum*. The wire is rigidly attached to a support at its upper end and the body is so attached that its center of gravity lies on the axis of the wire. As long as the elastic limit of the wire in shear is not exceeded, the angular displacement θ is proportional to the restoring torque in the opposite direction. Since the angular acceleration α is proportional to the torque, it follows that

$$\alpha = -k\theta$$

where k is the constant of proportionality. Let ω_0 be the angular velocity of the system

Fig. 327.

as it passes through the mid position OA, and ω the angular velocity as it passes through any other position OB for which the angular displacement is θ. Since

$$\omega d\omega = \alpha d\theta$$

$$\frac{\omega d\omega}{d\theta} = \alpha = -k\theta$$

$$\int_{\omega_0}^{\omega} \omega d\omega = -k \int_0^{\theta} \theta d\theta$$

$$\omega = \sqrt{\omega_0^2 - k\theta^2}$$

If θ_1 represents the maximum displacement, the corresponding angular velocity is zero. Hence,

$$0 = \sqrt{\omega_0^2 - k\theta_1^2}$$

$$\omega_0 = \sqrt{k} \cdot \theta_1$$

$$\omega = \sqrt{k(\theta_1^2 - \theta^2)}$$

Since $\omega = d\theta/dt$, the above equation becomes

$$dt = \frac{d\theta}{\sqrt{k(\theta_1{}^2 - \theta^2)}}$$

Now if the time is measured from the mid position,

$$\int_0^t dt = \int_0^\theta \frac{d\theta}{\sqrt{k(\theta_1{}^2 - \theta^2)}}$$

$$t = \frac{1}{\sqrt{k}} \sin^{-1} \frac{\theta}{\theta_1}$$

The time from mid position to the position of maximum displacement θ_1 is

$$t_1 = \frac{1}{\sqrt{k}} \sin^{-1} \frac{\theta_1}{\theta_1} = \frac{\pi}{2\sqrt{k}}$$

Since this represents the time for one-quarter of an oscillation, the period T of a complete oscillation becomes

$$T = \frac{2\pi}{\sqrt{k}}$$

If the torque required to produce the angular displacement θ_1 is denoted by C_1, and the moment of inertia of the body with respect to the axis of rotation by I, then

$$C_1 = -I\alpha = I k \theta_1$$

$$k = \frac{C_1}{I\theta_1}$$

The period T thus becomes

$$T = 2\pi \sqrt{\frac{I\theta_1}{C_1}}$$

Fig. 328.

The moment of inertia of a body of irregular shape may be determined experimentally by means of the torsion pendulum. The apparatus for this purpose consists of two disks firmly connected as shown in Fig. 328, with the upper disk rigidly fastened to the wire and the lower disk supporting the object whose moment of inertia is required, so placed that its center of gravity is at the axis of the wire. If I_1 represents the moment of inertia of the apparatus alone and T_1 its period, then

$$T_1 = 2\pi \sqrt{\frac{I_1 \theta_1}{C_1}}$$

Since the ratio θ_1/C_1 is a constant for the wire within its elastic limit,

$$T_1 = K \sqrt{I_1} \tag{1}$$

where K is a constant.

Similarly, if I represents the moment of inertia of the body and T the period of body and apparatus together,

$$T = K \sqrt{I_1 + I} \tag{2}$$

By combining equations (1) and (2), the following relations are obtained,

$$\frac{T_1}{T} = \sqrt{\frac{I_1}{I_1 + I}}$$

$$I = I_1 \left[\frac{T^2}{T_1{}^2} - 1 \right]$$

If the value θ_1/C_1 can be determined, I_1 may be obtained from equation (1) after observing the period of oscillation of the apparatus alone. If the apparatus is of such form that its moment of inertia I_1 can be computed directly, it will not be necessary to determine the value θ_1/C_1.

Problems

1. A torsion pendulum consists of a cast-iron plate 1 ft. square and 1 in. thick, suspended at its center by a steel wire 5 ft. long and $\frac{1}{8}$ in. in diameter. What torque is required to produce a displacement of 30°? Compute the period of oscillation. Modulus of elasticity in shear, $E = 12,000,000$ lb. per sq. in.   *Ans.* 0.209 ft-lb.; 4.38 sec.

2. The disks of the torsion pendulum shown in Fig. 328 have a diameter of 2 ft. and a combined weight of 120 lb. The unloaded pendulum is observed to make 25 oscillations in 1 min. A connecting rod whose moment of inertia is required is placed on the lower disk with its center of gravity at the axis of the wire and the combination is now observed to make 15 oscillations in 1 min. Compute the moment of inertia of the connecting rod with respect

to its centroidal axis.   (Assume the weight of the vertical rods between the
disks to be negligible.)   *Ans.* 3.32.

Supplementary Problems

1. The rotating parts of the hoist shown in Fig. 329 weigh 600 lb. and
have a radius of gyration of 1.8 ft.   The loaded car has a velocity of 22 ft.
per sec. down the incline just before the band brake is applied.   Car resistance is 8 lb. per ton, and the coefficient of friction for the band brake is 0.35.

Fig. 329.

What force P on the brake lever is required to decelerate the car at the rate
of 2 ft. per sec. per sec.?   Neglect the bearing friction.   *Ans.* 55.6 lb.

2. The rim of a cast-iron flywheel has 6-ft. diameter outside, 5-ft. diameter
inside, and 1 ft. width.   The axle has 4-in. diameter and rotates in bearings
for which the coefficient of friction is 0.015.   Neglecting the mass of hub and
spokes, in what time will the
flywheel come to rest from a
speed of 225 r.p.m. under the
action of friction alone?

Ans. 37 min. 11 sec.

3. Two cast-iron balls, each
12 in. in diameter, are connected
by a stiff rod and rotate about
a vertical axis midway between
them as shown in Fig. 330.
Neglecting bearing friction and
the mass of rod and axle, what
weight W will give the spheres
an angular velocity of 600 r.p.m. in 20 sec., starting from rest?

Ans. 228 lb.

Fig. 330.

4. A circular steel disk of 3-ft. diameter and 2-in. thickness is mounted
on a horizontal axis through an element of its curved surface.   It is held at
rest with its center vertically above the axis, then released, and allowed to
rotate under the influence of gravity alone.   Compute the normal and tangential components of the reaction at the support as the disk passes through

(a) a position 120° from the starting position; (b) a position 180° from the starting position.

Ans. (a) R_n = 1440 lb., R_t = 167 lb.; (b) R_n = 2110 lb., R_t = 0.

5. The disk of Prob. 4 above is cut into two equal semicircular portions. One of these is mounted on a horizontal axis coinciding with its geometric axis. It is held at rest with its center of gravity vertically above the axis, then released, and allowed to rotate under the influence of gravity alone. Compute the normal and tangential components of the reaction at the support as the disk passes through a position (a) 90° from the starting position; (b) 180° from the starting position.

Ans. (a) R_n = 208 lb., R_t = 185 lb.; (b) R_n = 705 lb., R_t = 0 lb.

6. Determine the period of oscillation of the semicircular disk described in Prob. 5. *Ans.* 1.47 sec.

7. Show that for a slender rod of length l, suspended from a vertical axis through its upper end, the limiting speed of rotation in revolutions per minute for which lifting impends is given by $n = \dfrac{15}{\pi}\sqrt{\dfrac{6g}{l}}$.

8. If the rod described in Prob. 7 above is rotated at a speed twice that for which lifting impends, to what angle with the vertical will it rise?

Ans. 75.5°.

9. What are the speed of rotation about the vertical axis and the tension in the supporting cables of the swing shown in Fig. 331 when the angle θ is 60°?

Ans. 20.8 r.p.m.; $2W$ lb.

10. A shaft 8 ft. long carries at 2 ft. from the left end a steel disk 18 in. in diameter and 3 in. thick, keyed to the shaft and 6 in. eccentric. At 2 ft. from the right end is keyed a similar disk at 90° behind the first. The system is to be balanced by placing counterweights at 12-in. radial distance in planes at the ends of the shaft.

FIG. 331.

Determine the balancing weights required and their angular position.

Ans. 85.4 lb.; 162°; 108°.

11. If the maximum tensile strength of cast iron is 20,000 lb. per sq. in., at what speed in revolutions per minute will rupture occur in a cast-iron flywheel whose rim is 12 in. wide, 4 in. thick, and 10 ft. in outside diameter? Neglect tension in the spokes. *Ans.* 898 r.p.m.

12. If the allowable tensile stress for cast iron is 3000 lb. per sq. in., what is the limiting diameter of cast-iron flywheels rotating at 300 r.p.m., assuming tension in spokes to be neglected? *Ans.* 11.2 ft.

13. In the weighted conical pendulum governor shown in Fig. 332, W_1 = 60 lb. and W = 20 lb. What is the speed of rotation for the position shown?

Ans. 137 r.p.m.

14. A compound pendulum consists of a semicircular steel disk of 6-in.

diameter and 1-in. thickness attached to a circular steel rod 18 in. long and 1 in. in diameter suspended from a horizontal axis through its upper end, as shown in Fig. 333. Compute the distance of the center of oscillation from the support, and the period of oscillation. *Ans.* 17 in.; 1.32 sec.

FIG. 332.   FIG. 333.

15. The connecting rod of a locomotive weighs 600 lb., and the distance of its center of gravity from the center of the crank pin is found to be 3 ft. Upon suspending the connecting rod from the crank pin and allowing it to oscillate as a compound pendulum, it is observed to make 25 complete vibrations in 60 sec. Compute the moment of inertia of the connecting rod with respect to the axis of the crank pin and also with respect to the parallel centroidal axis. *Ans.* 263; 95.

CHAPTER XII

PLANE MOTION

Art. 91. Plane Motion. When a body moves in such a manner that all points in the body describe paths lying in parallel planes, the motion is known as plane motion. The plane in which the center of gravity moves is usually taken as the reference plane. Such motion in general consists of a combination of translation and rotation as is evident in a rolling wheel, the connecting rod of an engine, etc. If the motion of some point of reference within a body having plane motion is known, the motion of any other point in the body may be determined by the principle of relative motion, as discussed in Art. 92. It can also be shown that any plane motion at a given instant may be reduced to one of rotation only about an axis known as the *instantaneous axis*. The use of the instantaneous axis in determining the motion of any point in the body will be discussed in Art. 93.

Art. 92. Relative Motion. The motion of a body referred to a point fixed in space is known as its absolute motion. The motion of a body referred to a point which is itself in motion is known as its motion relative to the given moving point. Thus, the displacement, velocity, or acceleration of a body may be absolute or relative. Although the earth is in motion through space, it is customary, in dealing with objects moving on the earth, to regard points on the earth's surface as fixed. The motion of a body with respect to a point fixed on the earth is then regarded as absolute.

If the velocity of a point B relative to a moving point A be added vectorially to the absolute velocity of A, the vector sum will be the absolute velocity of B.

Absolute velocity of A + Velocity of B relative to A =
Absolute velocity of B

The same proposition is equally true when displacement or acceleration is substituted for velocity. It should be particularly noted that the addition indicated must be performed vectorially. The principle of relative motion may be used to advantage in many problems involving motion of two or more objects.

Example

In Fig. 334 (a), A is the cross head, B the crank pin, AB the connecting rod, and O the center of the flywheel of a reciprocating engine. The connecting rod is 3 ft. long, and the crank radius is 1 ft. Determine the

Fig. 334.

absolute velocity of the cross head A when the speed of rotation of the flywheel is 120 r.p.m. and the crank pin B is 60° from dead center, as shown.

Solution: The absolute velocity of the crank pin B is at 90° with the crank radius OB. It is therefore at 30° with the horizontal, and its magnitude is

$$v_B = r\omega = 1 \cdot \left(\frac{120}{60}\right) \times 2\pi = 12.56 \text{ ft. per sec.}$$

The cross head A is forced to move between horizontal guides, and therefore the direction of the absolute velocity of A is known to be horizontal.

The crank pin B is always at a fixed distance of 3 ft. from A. Therefore the direction of the velocity of B relative to A must be at 90° with AB and consequently at angle α with the vertical. From the diagram:

$$\alpha = \sin^{-1} \frac{1 \sin 60°}{3} = \sin^{-1} .289 = 16.8°$$

The directions of all three of the velocities involved are now known, together with the magnitude of one of them; the vector triangle is thus determined as shown in Fig. 334 (b). The value of v_A may be determined graphically from the triangle; or trigonometrically, by the sine law, as follows:

$$\frac{v_A}{\sin 43.2°} = \frac{12.56}{\sin 106.8°}$$

$$v_A = 8.98 \text{ ft. per sec.}$$

Problems

1. A boat which can develop a speed of 20 mi. per hr. in still water is directed straight across a river 2400 ft. wide whose velocity is 3 mi. per hr. How long will it take to cross the river? Where, and with what velocity, will it strike the opposite bank?

Ans. 1 min. 22 sec.; 360 ft. downstream; 20.2 mi. per hr.

2. At what angle must the boat in Prob. 1 be directed upstream in order to land directly across the river?   *Ans.* 8.62°.

3. Solve Prob. 1 if the boat is directed 30° upstream.

Ans. 1 min. 35 sec.; 970 ft. upstream; 18.7 mi. per hr.

4. An ice boat is to attain a velocity of 50 mi. per hr. due east when the wind from the north has a velocity of 30 mi. per hr. At what angle with the direction of the boat must the sail be placed to make this possible? Assume friction to be negligible.   *Ans.* 31°.

5. Solve the Example above if the crank angle is 120° instead of 60°.

Ans. 12.8 ft. per sec.

FIG. 335.

6. The water-driven turbine shown in Fig. 335 is rotating at 600 r.p.m. The water enters with a velocity of 80 ft. per sec. at an angle of 60° with the radius extended. If the outside radius of the wheel is 1 ft., at what angle θ should the blade be curved at the outer edge for smooth entrance?

Ans. 9.16°.

Art. 93. Instantaneous Center.

It was pointed out in Art. 91 that any plane motion of a body can be reduced to one of rotation only about an axis called the instantaneous axis. The intersection of the instantaneous axis with the plane of reference is called the *instantaneous center*. If the direction of the absolute velocities of any two points in the body is known, the location of the instantaneous center may be found. Let v_A and v_B, Fig. 336, represent the respective velocities of points A and B in a rigid body having plane motion. If the motion of the body can be reduced to one of rotation only, the center about which A rotates must lie on a line through A normal to the direction of the velocity v_A. Likewise,

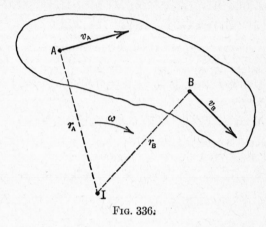

FIG. 336.

the center about which B rotates must lie on a line through B normal to the direction of the velocity v_B. The intersection I

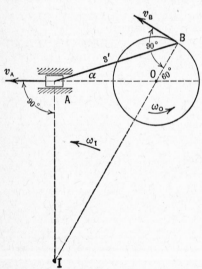

FIG. 337.

of these two lines must therefore be the instantaneous center of rotation for the body. This point does not in general remain fixed in position with respect to the body or to space.

If the angular velocity of the body with respect to the instantaneous axis is denoted by ω, then $v_A = r_A\omega$ and $v_B = r_B\omega$.

Example

Solve the example of Art. 92, making use of the instantaneous center.

Solution: The instantaneous center of rotation for the connecting rod AB, Fig. 337, is located at I, the intersection of the normals to the absolute velocities of points A and B.

In the triangle AOB, the angle α is 16.8°, as previously determined. Angle ABO is thus 43.2°, and angle AIB is 30°. Now applying the sine law to triangle ABI,

$$\frac{AI}{\sin 43.2°} = \frac{3}{\sin 30°} = \frac{BI}{\sin 106.8°}$$

$$AI = 4.11 \text{ ft.}; \ BI = 5.74 \text{ ft.}$$

The absolute linear velocity of B is 12.56 ft. per sec. as previously determined. Hence the angular velocity of B with respect to the instantaneous center is,

$$\omega_I = v_B/BI = 12.56/5.74 = 2.18 \text{ rad. per sec.}$$

This is also the angular velocity of the body. Hence, the absolute linear velocity of A is

$$v_A = AI \cdot \omega_I = 4.11 \times 2.18 = 8.98 \text{ ft. per sec.}$$

Problems

1. Solve the above example if the crank angle is 120° instead of 60°.

Ans. 12.8 ft. per sec.

2. A wheel 3 ft. in diameter, Fig. 338, rolls without slipping on a horizontal track. The linear velocity of the center C of the wheel is 20 ft. per sec. toward the right. Locate the instantaneous center and determine, by its use, the absolute velocities of points A, B, and D.

FIG. 338.

Ans. $v_A = 0$; $v_B = 40$ ft. per sec.; $v_D = 28.3$ ft. per sec. at 45° below the horizontal.

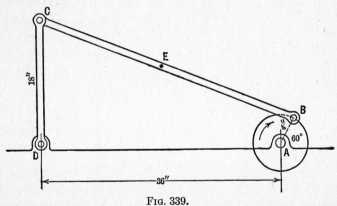

FIG. 339.

3. In the mechanism shown in Fig. 339, the wheel A rotates at 450 r.p.m.

Determine the absolute velocity of point C and the angular velocity of link CD when in the position shown.   *Ans.* 16.6 ft. per sec.; 11.1 rad. per sec.

4. Compute the absolute velocity of the center of gravity E of the link BC shown in Fig. 339. $CE = 20$ in.   *Ans.* 15.6 ft. per sec.

Art. 94. Equations of Plane Motion.

In Fig. 340 is shown a rigid body, with center of gravity at C, rotating about an axis through any point O with angular velocity ω and angular accelera-

Fig. 340.

tion α, the axis of rotation itself having motion of translation with velocity v and acceleration a. A particle of mass dM at radial distance ρ from O is shown. Owing to the rotation of the body, the particle will have a tangential acceleration $\rho\alpha$ and a normal acceleration $\rho\omega^2$. Owing to the translation of the body, the particle will have an acceleration a, parallel to the direction of translation. The effective forces acting on the particle to produce these accelerations are $dM\rho\alpha$ in the tangential direction, $dM\rho\omega^2$ in the normal direction, and dMa in the direction of the translation. The point O is taken as the origin of coordinates with the x axis in the direction of translation. The following equations are then obtained:

$$\Sigma F_x = \int dM\, a + \int dM\rho\alpha \sin\theta + \int dM\rho\omega^2 \cos\theta \qquad (1)$$

$$\Sigma F_y = \int dM\rho\alpha \cos\theta - \int dM\rho\omega^2 \sin\theta \qquad (2)$$

$$\Sigma M_0 = \int dMa\cdot\rho \sin\theta + \int dM\rho\alpha\cdot\rho \qquad (3)$$

Since a, α, and ω are common to all points in the body, and since $\rho \sin\theta = y$, and $\rho \cos\theta = x$, the above equations become:

$$\Sigma F_x = a \int dM + \alpha \int y\, dM + \omega^2 \int x\, dM \qquad (4)$$

$$\Sigma F_y = \alpha \int x \, dM - \omega^2 \int y \, dM \tag{5}$$

$$\Sigma M_0 = a \int y \, dM + \alpha \int \rho^2 dM \tag{6}$$

Now, $\int dM = M$, $\int y \, dM = M \bar{y}$, $\int x \, dM = M \bar{x}$, and $\int \rho^2 dM = I_0$, so that the equations now become:

$$\Sigma F_x = Ma + M\bar{y}\alpha + M\bar{x}\omega^2 \tag{7}$$

$$\Sigma F_y = M\bar{x}\alpha - M\bar{y}\omega^2 \tag{8}$$

$$\Sigma M_0 = M\bar{y}a + I_0\alpha \tag{9}$$

The above equations (7) to (9) are the general equations for plane motion.

Art. 95. Rolling Bodies. The equations (7) to (9) of Art. 94 may be further simplified if the axis of rotation is taken through the center of gravity. When this is done, $\bar{x} = 0$, $\bar{y} = 0$, a becomes $\bar{a}$, I_0 becomes I_C, and the equations of motion become:

$$\mathbf{\Sigma F_x = M \, \bar{a}} \tag{1}$$

$$\mathbf{\Sigma F_y = 0} \tag{2}$$

$$\mathbf{\Sigma M_C = I_C \alpha} \tag{3}$$

The above equations may be applied to any rolling body provided the axis of reference is taken through the center of gravity. Their application will now be shown.

Example 1

A solid cylinder of 3-ft. diameter and weighing 400 lb. is pulled up a 30° incline by a force $P = 300$ lb., as shown in Fig. 341. Assuming that the cylinder rolls freely (without slipping), determine the linear

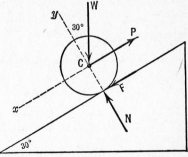

Fig. 341.

acceleration of the center of gravity of the cylinder and the static frictional force F developed between cylinder and incline.

Solution: The cylinder will be considered as rotating about an axis through its center which in turn will have a linear acceleration directed up the slope. The x axis is taken parallel to the line of motion, and equations (1) to (3) above are applied:

$$\Sigma F_x = 300 - 400 \sin 30° - F = \frac{400}{32.2} a$$

$$\Sigma F_y = N - 400 \cos 30° = 0$$

$$\Sigma M_C = F \times 1.5 = [\tfrac{1}{2}(400/32.2)(1.5)^2]\alpha$$

Also:

$$a = r\alpha = 1.5\alpha$$

Simultaneous solution of the above equations gives

$$a = 5.37 \text{ ft. per sec}^2.; \quad F = 33.3 \text{ lb.}$$

Example 2

A solid cylinder rolls down a plane inclined at angle θ with the horizontal. Show that $f = \tfrac{1}{3} \tan \theta$ is the minimum value of the coefficient of friction which will prevent slipping.

Fig. 342.

Solution: The forces acting on the cylinder are shown in Fig. 342. The equations of plane motion become:

$$\Sigma F_x = W \sin \theta - F = \frac{Wa}{g} \tag{1}$$

$$\Sigma F_y = N - W \cos \theta = 0 \tag{2}$$

$$\Sigma M_C = F \cdot r = \frac{1}{2} \frac{W}{g} r^2 \alpha \tag{3}$$

Also

$$a = r\alpha \tag{4}$$

and

$$F = fN \tag{5}$$

Simultaneous solution of the above equations gives $f = \frac{1}{3} \tan \theta$. For values of f less than the above, partial slipping will occur.

Example 3

The roller in Fig. 343 weighs 200 lb. and has a radius of gyration of 3/4 ft. If the roller is released from rest and rolls freely, compute the linear velocity of its center of gravity after it has moved 10 ft.

Fig. 343.

Solution: Letting T represent the unknown cable tension and a the unknown linear acceleration of the center of gravity, the equations of plane motion for the roller become:

$$\Sigma F_x = T - F = \frac{200}{32.2}\, a \qquad (1)$$

$$\Sigma F_y = N - 200 = 0 \qquad (2)$$

$$\Sigma M_C = T \times \frac{1}{2} + F \times 1 = \left[\frac{200}{32.2}\left(\frac{3}{4}\right)^2\right]\alpha \qquad (3)$$

Also

$$a = r\alpha = 1 \cdot \alpha = \alpha \qquad (4)$$

The acceleration of the 50-lb. counterweight will, by inspection or by use of the instantaneous center, be $1\frac{1}{2}$ times that of the center of the roller. If the reversed effective force is added to this body, a vertical summation of forces gives

$$T + \frac{50(\frac{3}{2}a)}{32.2} = 50 \qquad (5)$$

Simultaneous solution of equations (1) to (5) gives

$$F = 1.5 \text{ lb.}; \quad T = 36.8 \text{ lb.}; \quad a = 5.69 \text{ ft. per sec.}^2$$

Finally:

$$v^2 = v_0^2 + 2as$$
$$v^2 = 0 + 2(5.69)(10) = 113.8$$
$$v = 10.7 \text{ ft. per sec.}$$

Problems

1. A cylinder starts from rest and rolls freely down a 30° incline 10 ft. long. In what time will it reach the bottom?   *Ans.* 1.37 sec.

2. Solve Prob. 1 if the cylinder is replaced by a sphere.   *Ans.* 1.32 sec.

3. A cylinder starts up a 20° incline with a velocity of 10 ft. per sec. Assuming that no slipping occurs, how far will the cylinder roll?

Ans. 6.80 ft.

4. The roller shown in Fig. 344 weighs 50 lb. and has a radius of gyration of 1.5 ft. If it starts from rest and rolls freely, determine its angular velocity at the end of 10 sec. and the frictional force.

Ans. 49.5 rad. per sec.; 17.3 lb.

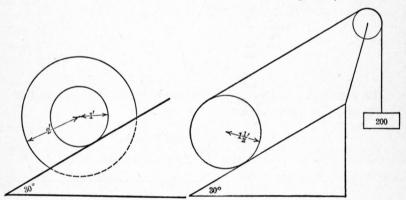

FIG. 344.   FIG. 345.

5. A 100-lb. cylinder of 2-ft. diameter starts from rest on a 45° incline. The coefficient of kinetic friction is 0.2; the coefficient of static friction is 0.22. Compute the force of friction, the linear velocity of the center, and angular velocity of the cylinder, after it has traveled 15 ft.

Ans. 14.1 lb.; 23.3 ft. per sec.; 11.6 rad. per sec.

6. A solid sphere rolls down a plane inclined at angle θ with the horizontal. Determine the minimum value of the coefficient of friction which will prevent slipping.   *Ans.* $f = \frac{2}{7} \tan \theta$.

7. Solve Ex. 3 above if the rope comes off the lower side of the drum attached to the roller.   *Ans.* 7.03 ft. per sec.

8. The roller in Fig. 345 is a solid cylinder weighing 600 lb. with the rope wrapped around it. Assuming that no slipping occurs, compute the cable tension, the friction, and the linear velocity of the center of the roller after moving 20 ft. from rest.   *Ans.* 177 lb.; 159 lb.; 8.7 ft. per sec.

Art. 96. Kinetic Energy of Plane Motion. A rigid body having plane motion is shown in Fig. 346 (*a*). The motion consists of rotation with angular velocity ω about an axis through point O combined with translation of the axis with linear velocity v_0. Any particle of mass dM within the body will have two component velocities, $v_t = \rho\omega$ in the tangential direction, and v_0 parallel and equal to the velocity of O. The resultant velocity of dM is

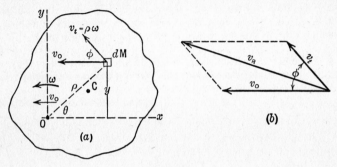

Fig. 346.

the vector sum of these two components or v_R as shown in Fig. 346 (*b*). By the cosine law:

$$v_R{}^2 = v_0{}^2 + v_t{}^2 + 2v_0 \cdot v_t \cdot \cos\phi$$

$$= v_0{}^2 + \rho^2\omega^2 + 2v_0 \cdot \rho\omega \cdot \sin\theta$$

$$= v_0{}^2 + \rho^2\omega^2 + 2v_0\omega \cdot y$$

Since the kinetic energy of the particle is $\frac{1}{2}dM v_R{}^2$, the total kinetic energy of the body is:

$$K.E. = \int \tfrac{1}{2}dM\, v_R{}^2$$

$$K.E. = \int \tfrac{1}{2}\, dM\, v_0{}^2 + \int \tfrac{1}{2}dM\rho^2\omega^2 + \int dM\, v_0\omega y$$

Since v_0 and ω are common to all particles, the preceding equation becomes:

$$K.E. = \tfrac{1}{2}v_0{}^2 \int dM + \tfrac{1}{2}\omega^2 \int \rho^2 dM + v_0\omega \int y dM$$

$$= \tfrac{1}{2}Mv_0{}^2 + \tfrac{1}{2}I_0\omega^2 + v_0\omega M\bar{y}$$

Now, if the axis of rotation is taken through the center of gravity C, $\bar{y} = 0$ and the total kinetic energy becomes

$$\textbf{K.E.} = \tfrac{1}{2}\,\textbf{M}\bar{\textbf{v}}^2 + \tfrac{1}{2}\,\textbf{I}_\textbf{C}\boldsymbol{\omega}^2$$

Thus, the total kinetic energy of a body having plane motion may be considered as the sum of its kinetic energy of translation and its kinetic energy of rotation about an axis through its center of gravity.

The work-energy equation as previously applied to rectilinear motion and to motion of rotation may also be applied to plane motion.

Example 1

A sphere starts from rest and rolls freely down a 30° incline 40 ft. long. Determine the linear velocity of its center of gravity as it reaches the foot of the slope.

Solution: The initial kinetic energy of the sphere is zero. Positive work is done by gravity. No negative work is done since the frictional force necessary to prevent slipping is static and produces no displacement. The final kinetic energy is the sum of the energies of translation and rotation. The work-energy equation thus becomes:

$$0 + W \cdot 40 \sin 30 - 0 = \frac{1}{2}\frac{W}{32.2}\,v^2 + \frac{1}{2}\left[\frac{2}{5}\frac{W}{32.2}\,r^2\right]\left(\frac{v}{r}\right)^2$$

$$v = 30.3 \text{ ft. per sec.}$$

Example 2

The roller in Fig. 347 weighs 200 lb. and has a radius of gyration of $\frac{3}{4}$ ft. If the roller is released from rest and rolls freely, compute the linear velocity of its center after it has moved 10 ft.

Solution: The initial kinetic energy of the system is zero. Positive work is done by gravity on the 50-lb. counterweight. No negative work is done. The final kinetic energy of the system includes the energy of translation of the roller, the energy of rotation of the roller, and the energy of translation of the counterweight.

By inspection it is seen that the displacement and velocity of the counterweight will each be $1\frac{1}{2}$ times that of the roller. The resulting work-energy equation is then:

$$0 + 50 \times 15 - 0 = \frac{1}{2}\frac{200}{32.2}v^2 + \frac{1}{2}\left[\frac{200}{32.2}\left(\frac{3}{4}\right)^2\right]\left(\frac{v}{1}\right)^2 + \frac{1}{2}\frac{50}{32.2}(1.5v)^2$$

$$v = 10.7 \text{ ft. per sec.}$$

FIG. 347.

This solution should be compared with that of Ex. 3, Art. 95.

Problems

1. Solve Prob. 3, Art. 95, by the work-energy method.

2. Solve for the angular velocity of the roller in Prob. 4, Art. 95, by the work-energy method.

3. Solve for the velocity of the roller in Prob. 8, Art. 95, by the work-energy method.

4. A sphere of 8-in. diameter is given an initial linear velocity of 15 ft. per sec. along a horizontal surface. If the coefficient of rolling resistance is 0.1 in., how far will the sphere roll?

$\qquad\qquad$ *Ans.* 196 ft.

5. A cylinder 4 ft. in diameter and weighing 50 lb. has a drum of 2-ft. diameter attached as shown in Fig. 348. A 5-lb. horizontal pull is applied by means of a rope wrapped around the drum and coming off the lower side. Which way will the cylinder roll? If the weight of the drum is negligible

FIG. 348.

and no slipping occurs, determine the angular velocity of the cylinder after rolling 10 ft. from rest. $\qquad$ *Ans.* 2.31 rad. per sec. clockwise.

6. Determine the angle of inclination of force P in Fig. 348, so that the cylinder will slide without rolling. $\qquad$ *Ans.* 60° with the horizontal.

Supplementary Problems

1. The drive wheel of a locomotive is 6 ft. in diameter, and the crank radius is 15 in. If the locomotive is running at a speed of 45 mi. per hr., determine the absolute velocity of the crank pin (a) when it is horizontally in front of the center of the wheel; (b) when it is directly below the center of the wheel; (c) when it is behind and 30° above the center of the wheel. *Ans.* (a) 71.5 ft. per sec. at 22.6° below the horizontal; (b) 38.5 ft. per sec. forward; (c) 83.3 ft. per sec. at 16.6° above the horizontal.

2. Steam with a velocity of 2000 ft. per sec. enters a turbine through a nozzle placed at 20° with the plane of motion of the rotor, as shown in Fig. 349. If the mean radius of the wheel, measured from its center to the mid-

FIG. 349.

point of the buckets, is 13.1 in., and the wheel rotates at 3600 r.p.m., at what angle θ should the buckets be curved at the outer edge for smooth entrance? *Ans.* 25°.

3. In the quick-return shaper mechanism shown in Fig. 350, B is a block which is pinned to the wheel D and slides within the slotted arm AC, causing it to oscillate about the fixed center A as the wheel rotates. If the wheel D rotates at 30 r.p.m., determine the velocity of B relative to the arm AC, and the absolute velocity of C, when the angle θ is 150°.

Ans. 1.45 ft. per sec. toward A; 2.16 ft. per sec. at 16.1° with horizontal.

4. Solve for the absolute velocity of C in Prob. 3, (a) when θ = 90°; (b) when θ = 270°.   *Ans.* 2.69 ft. per sec.; 6.28 ft. per sec.

5. The connecting rod in Fig. 351 is 20 in. long, and the radius of the crank is 8 in. If the flywheel is rotating at 150 r.p.m., determine the velocity of the cross head when θ = 45°. Solve by use of relative motion and check by use of the instantaneous center.   *Ans.* 9.58 ft. per sec.

6. A cylinder 1 ft. in diameter and weighing 60 lb. has a cord wrapped around it and attached to a support above, as shown in Fig. 352. If the cylinder is released from rest and allowed to fall, determine the linear acceleration and the tension in the cord. From the acceleration, determine the linear velocity of the center of gravity after it has fallen 5 ft. Check the velocity by the work-energy method.

Ans. 21.5 ft. per sec.²; 20.0 lb.; 14.6 ft. per sec.

7. Solve Prob. 6 if the cord passes around a pulley at the top and returns

to the center of the cylinder as shown in Fig. 353.   Neglect the mass of the
pulley.   *Ans.* 10.7 ft. per sec.^{2}; 20 lb.; 10.3 ft. per sec.

FIG. 350.

FIG. 351.

FIG. 352.

FIG. 353.

8. A wheel and its axle weigh 200 lb. and have a radius of gyration of
1.5 ft.   The wheel is placed with the projecting parts of the axles resting on
tracks inclined to 30° with the horizontal as shown in Fig. 354.   What coefficient of friction is required to prevent slipping as the wheel rolls down the
track?   Assuming that no slipping occurs, determine the angular velocity of
the wheel after rolling 10 ft.   *Ans.* 0.520; 108 r.p.m.

9. The wheel described in Prob. 8 is pulled up the inclined track by a force P applied at the center of the wheel and acting parallel to the track. Determine the force P required to give the center of the wheel a linear acceleration of 0.5 ft. per sec.[2] Assuming that no slipping occurs, determine the friction at the rolling surface.   *Ans.* 131 lb.; 28 lb.

Fig. 354.   Fig. 355.

10. A 20-lb. block is suspended from a cord wrapped around a cylinder which rolls on a horizontal track as shown in Fig. 355. The cylinder has a 3-ft. diameter and weighs 150 lb. If the cylinder starts from rest and rolls without slipping, compute its angular velocity after it has rolled 10 ft.

Ans. 44.3 r.p.m.

11. A hollow cylinder having 18-in. outside diameter and 15-in. inside diameter starts from rest and rolls freely down a 15° slope 40 ft. long. With what velocity and in what time will it reach the foot of the slope? Solve by means of the equations of plane motion and check by means of work-energy.

Ans. 19.0 ft. per sec.; 4.21 sec.

12. Solve Prob. 11 if rolling resistance is taken into consideration, the coefficient being 0.05 in.   *Ans.* 18.8 ft. per sec.; 4.26 sec.

13. How far along a horizontal surface will the hollow cylinder of Prob. 12 continue to roll after reaching the foot of the slope?   *Ans.* 1830 ft.

CHAPTER XIII

IMPULSE, MOMENTUM, AND IMPACT

Art. 97. Linear Impulse and Momentum. The effect of forces on the motion of bodies has been determined thus far by the force, mass, and acceleration method (Chap. VIII), and by the work-energy method (Chap. X). A third method, utilizing impulse and momentum, is of advantage in certain problems and will now be considered.

The *impulse* of a force is the product of the force and the time during which it acts. Thus, if a force F is constant in magnitude and direction during time t, its impulse is given by the statement:

$$\text{Linear impulse} = \mathbf{F} \cdot \mathbf{t} \approx MLT^{-1}$$

If the force is variable in magnitude, the impulse may be taken for a differential time dt and then integrated to determine the total impulse $\int_0^t F \, dt$. Impulse is a vector quantity and subject to the laws governing vectors in general. The direction of the impulse vector is the same as that of the force involved. There is no special name for the unit of impulse, and it is therefore expressed in terms of the force and time units in use. Thus the customary unit in engineering work is the pound-second.

The linear *momentum* of a body is the product of its mass and velocity. Thus,

$$\text{Linear momentum} = \mathbf{M}\mathbf{v} \approx MLT^{-1}$$

Momentum is a vector quantity also, the direction being the same as that of the change of velocity involved. There is no special name for the unit of momentum; but, since linear momentum has the same dimensions as linear impulse, it may be expressed in the same units. As stated above, the customary unit is the pound-second.

The relation between the impulse of a force acting upon a body

243

and the change of momentum of the body is based on Newton's second law of motion, the mathematical expression of which, as stated in Chap. VIII, is $F = Ma$, where F represents the resultant or unbalanced force acting on the body and a the acceleration produced. Let both sides of the equation be multiplied by dt. Then

$$F \, dt = M \, a \, dt$$

Since, $a = dv/dt$ by definition, the above equation becomes

$$F \, dt = M \, dv$$

Let the limits be 0 and t for time and v_0 and v for velocity. Then, if the mass is constant,

$$\int_0^t F \, dt = M \int_{v_0}^v dv = Mv - Mv_0$$

If the force is constant,

$$\mathbf{Ft = Mv - Mv_0}$$

It is thus seen that the linear impulse of a force acting upon a body is equal to the change of linear momentum. If a body is acted upon by several forces, the change of momentum is equal to the vector sum of the separate impulses received.

The above relation is particularly useful in problems where force, mass, velocity, and time are involved. It is also valuable in analyzing situations involving impulsive forces, that is, forces acting for infinitesimal or indefinitely small intervals of time.

Fig. 356.

Example 1

Determine the drawbar pull required to increase the velocity of a 50-ton car on a 1 per cent grade from 30 mi. per hr. to 60 mi. per hr. in 2 min. if the train resistance is 8 lb. per ton.

Solution: The forces acting on the car, including the total train resistance of 400 lb. and the unknown drawbar pull P, are shown in Fig. 356. The resultant force in the direction of motion is

$$F = P - 400 - 1000 = P - 1400$$

Since

$$Ft = Mv - Mv_0$$

$$(P - 1400)120 = \frac{100{,}000}{32.2} \times 88 - \frac{100{,}000}{32.2} \times 44$$

$$P = 2540 \text{ lb.}$$

Example 2

Water, under a head of 100 ft., issues from a nozzle of 1-in. diameter and impinges normally upon a flat vane which is moving with a velocity of 25 ft. per sec. in a direction away from the nozzle. Neglecting any losses, compute the impulsive force of the jet upon the vane.

Solution: The velocity of the water as it leaves the nozzle is

$$v_w = \sqrt{2gh} = \sqrt{2 \times g \times 100} = 80.2 \text{ ft. per sec.}$$

The force exerted on the vane is equal and opposite to the force F exerted by the plate on the stream of water, Fig. 357. Since this force remains constant as long as the original conditions prevail, any length of time may be assumed. It is convenient to assume the time interval as 1 sec.

FIG. 357.

The weight of water striking the moving vane in 1 sec. is

$$W = 62.5Q = 62.5A(v_w - v_p)$$

$$W = 62.5 \times \frac{\pi}{4}\left(\frac{1}{12}\right)^2 \times (80.2 - 25) = 18.8 \text{ lb. per sec.}$$

Since

$$Ft = Mv - Mv_0$$

$$-F \times 1 = \frac{18.8}{32.2}(25 - 80.2)$$

$$F = 32.2 \text{ lb.}$$

Problems

1. If the system shown in Fig. 358 starts from rest and the coefficient of friction is 0.2, determine the velocity after 8 sec. and the tension in the cord.

Ans. 81.0 ft. per sec.; 20.6 lb.

FIG. 358.   FIG. 359.

2. If the coefficient of friction for the block in Fig. 359 is 0.2, determine the velocity of the block 10 sec. after it starts from rest.

Ans. 9.66 ft. per sec.

3. If the force P acting on the block described in Prob. 2 is replaced by a variable horizontal force $P = 50 + t^2$, determine the velocity of the block 3 sec. after it starts from rest.   *Ans.* 6.28 ft. per sec.

4. A machine gun fires 300 bullets per minute. If each bullet weighs 0.1 lb. and the muzzle velocity is 2500 ft. per sec., compute the average recoil force exerted by the gun.   *Ans.* 38.8 lb.

5. A 2-in. diameter stream of water with a velocity of 120 ft. per sec. impinges normally upon a stationary flat vane. Compute the impulsive force exerted by the water upon the vane.   *Ans.* 610 lb.

6. If the vane in Prob. 5 has a velocity of 30 ft. per sec. toward the nozzle, compute the force.   *Ans.* 952 lb.

7. If the stream of water in Prob. 5 impinges tangentially on a stationary curved vane which changes the direction of the water by 90°, compute the resultant force exerted on the vane.   *Ans.* 862 lb. at 45°.

Art. 98. Conservation of Linear Momentum.

If the vector sum of the various separate impulses received by a body or system of bodies is zero, the change of momentum of the system must be zero. This situation exists when two bodies or two parts of the same body interact on each other. By Newton's third law of motion, the forces exerted by each body on the other are equal and opposite, and since the time of interaction must necessarily be the same, the impulses of the forces are equal but opposite in direction. Then, if no other external forces are acting during the period of contact, the resultant impulse received by the system is zero, and the total momentum of the system remains constant. If M_1 and M_2 represent the masses of two bodies, v_1 and v_2 their velocities before contact, v_1' and v_2' their velocities after contact, the above statement may be expressed algebraically as follows:

$$\mathbf{M}_1\mathbf{v}_1 + \mathbf{M}_2\mathbf{v}_2 = \mathbf{M}_1\mathbf{v}_1' + \mathbf{M}_2\mathbf{v}_2'$$

In using the above equation, the algebraic sign of each known velocity must be taken as positive or negative according to some previously chosen convention.   A velocity unknown in direction is assumed to be positive, and the sign of the result then determines the correct direction.

It is important to recognize the fact that, although there is no loss of momentum in the interaction of two bodies, there is always a loss of kinetic energy due to generation of heat.

Example

A gun weighing 100,000 lb. fires a projectile weighing 800 lb. with a muzzle velocity of 1200 ft. per sec.   Neglecting the effect of the powder charge, compute the initial recoil velocity of the gun, the kinetic energy of the projectile, and the kinetic energy of the gun.

Solution: Before the shot is fired, the momentum is zero for the gun and also for the projectile.   The conservation of momentum equation thus becomes

$$0 + 0 = \frac{100,000}{32.2}\, v_1' - \frac{800}{32.2} \times 1200$$

$$v_1' = 9.6 \text{ ft. per sec.}$$

The kinetic energy of the projectile is

$$\frac{1}{2}\frac{W}{g}\, v^2 = \frac{1}{2}\frac{800}{32.2}\,(1200)^2 = 17,900,000 \text{ ft-lb.}$$

The kinetic energy of the gun is

$$\frac{1}{2}\frac{W}{g}\, v^2 = \frac{1}{2} \times \frac{100,000}{32.2}\,(9.6)^2 = 143,000 \text{ ft-lb.}$$

The above results show that, although the gun and projectile have equal momentum, the kinetic energy of the projectile is about 125 times as great as that of the gun.

Problems

1. Solve the above example if the powder charge weighs 400 lb. and is assumed to have half the velocity of the projectile.

Ans. 12.0 ft. per sec.; 17,900,000 ft-lb.; 224,000 ft-lb.

2. A 60,000-lb. freight car with velocity of 5 mi. per hr. collides with another car weighing 80,000 lb. and having a velocity of 2 mi. per hr. in the opposite direction. During the collision the cars are automatically coupled together. Compute their common velocity after the collision and the change of kinetic energy for each car.

Ans. 1 mi. per hr.; − 48,000 ft-lb.; − 8020 ft-lb.

3. A 250,000-lb. gun fires a 1000-lb. projectile with a muzzle velocity of 2000 ft. per sec. Compute the initial recoil velocity of the gun. If the gun recoils a distance of 5 ft. against a constant force, determine the force.

Ans. 8 ft. per sec.; 49,700 lb.

4. A $\frac{1}{2}$-oz. bullet is fired horizontally into a 10-lb. block of wood resting on a horizontal surface for which the coefficient of friction is 0.3. If the block is moved a distance of 15 in. along the surface, what was the velocity of the bullet before striking?   *Ans.* 1570 ft. per sec.

FIG. 360.

5. The ballistic pendulum, consisting of a block of wood suspended by a light cord as shown in Fig. 360, is a device used at one time for measuring the velocity of small projectiles. The bullet is fired horizontally so as to strike the block at its center of percussion and is embedded in the block. (If the length of the cord is large compared to the depth of the block, the center of percussion will very nearly coincide with the geometric center of the block.) The angle θ to which the block swings after being struck is measured. If the bullet weighs 0.1 lb., the block weighs 20 lb., the center of the block is 10 ft. from the point of suspension, and the block swings 30° from the vertical, what was the velocity of the bullet?   *Ans.* 1870 ft. per sec.

Art. 99. Impact. The impulse of a force which acts during a very short interval of time (impulsive force) is sometimes called an *impact*. Since the forces exerted by two bodies on each other during collision are impulsive, the act of collision is commonly known as impact. Usually, the effect of the impulsive forces on the motion of the bodies is so large in comparison with that of other external forces that the effect of the latter may be neglected for the duration of the impact. Although the distance traveled during impact, the forces acting, and the time interval may all be unknown, it is possible by means of the principles of momentum to determine the changes of velocity.

Impact between two bodies may be direct or oblique, and central or eccentric. If the mass centers of the bodies, as they approach each other, move along the same straight line, the impact is direct; otherwise the impact is oblique. If the pressures exerted are along the line of mass centers, the impact is central; otherwise the impact is eccentric. Direct central impact will be considered first.

It has already been shown that the total momentum of the system remains constant during impact, as represented by the following equation.

$$M_1v_1 + M_2v_2 = M_1v_1' + M_2v_2' \tag{1}$$

A solution of problems in impact is possible by use of this equation alone if the two bodies have the same velocity after impact, that is, $v_1' = v_2'$. In general, however, this is not the case, and another relation between the velocities is required to complete the solution. This may be had from a consideration of the relative velocities of the two bodies during approach and during separation.

If the two bodies were perfectly elastic the relative velocity of separation would be equal to the relative velocity of approach. If the bodies were inelastic, no separation would occur and the relative velocity of separation would be zero. For partly elastic bodies, the relative velocity of separation is somewhat less than that of approach. Newton proved that the relative velocity of separation is directly proportional to the relative velocity of approach. The constant of proportionality depends on the materials and is called the *coefficient of restitution*. In Fig. 361 (a) the two bodies are approaching each other and have velocities v_1 and v_2 just before impact. The relative velocity of approach is $v_1 - v_2$.

Fig. 361.

In Fig. 361 (b), the bodies are in contact and have the same velocity. In Fig. 361 (c) the bodies have just separated and have velocities v_1' and v_2'. The relative velocity of separation is $v_2' - v_1'$. According to the definition stated above, the coefficient of restitution, denoted by e, is:

$$e = \frac{v_2' - v_1'}{v_1 - v_2}$$

This may also be written

$$v_2' - v_1' = e(v_1 - v_2) \tag{2}$$

For perfectly elastic bodies, the value of e is unity; for inelastic bodies, it is zero. For partly elastic bodies, its value may be found by experiment. A few values thus obtained are 0.95 for glass; 0.89 for ivory; 0.55 for steel; 0.50 for cast iron; and 0.15 for lead. Equations (1) and (2) are then sufficient to complete the solution. As previously explained, known velocities should be substituted into these equations as positive or negative according to some predetermined convention; the signs obtained for the unknown velocities in the final solution indicate the directions of these velocities.

The kinetic energy lost owing to impact is the difference between the kinetic energy of the system before impact and the kinetic energy of the system after impact.

In oblique impact, the velocities of approach may be resolved into components along the line of centers and normal to the line of centers. The normal components remain unchanged by impact. The components along the line of centers are then treated as in direct central impact, and the final components are then combined to obtain the final velocities.

Example

A 20-lb. body with velocity of 15 ft. per sec. collides with a 50-lb. body moving in the opposite direction with velocity of 5 ft. per sec. If the coefficient of restitution is 0.8, determine the magnitude and direction of the velocities after impact and the loss in kinetic energy.

Solution: The two bodies just before impact are shown in Fig. 362 (a). Velocity toward the right is taken as positive.

$v_1 = 15$ $v_2 = -5$

20   50   (a)

$v_1' = -10.7$ $v_2' = 5.28$

20   50   (b)

Fig. 362.

$$M_1 v_1 + M_2 v_2 = M_1 v_1' + M_2 v_2'$$

$$20 \times 15 - 50 \times 5 = 20 v_1' + 50 v_2' \qquad (1)$$

$$v_2' - v_1' = e(v_1 - v_2)$$

$$v_2' - v_1' = 0.8\,[15 - (-5)] \qquad (2)$$

Simultaneous solution of equations (1) and (2) gives

$$v_1' = -10.7 \text{ ft. per sec.}; \quad v_2' = +5.28 \text{ ft. per sec.}$$

In Fig. 362 (b), these velocities are shown in the directions corresponding to their respective signs.

The kinetic energy before impact is

$$K.E. = \frac{1}{2}\frac{20}{32.2}(15)^2 + \frac{1}{2}\frac{50}{32.2}(5)^2 = 89.4 \text{ ft-lb.}$$

The kinetic energy after impact is

$$K.E. = \frac{1}{2}\frac{20}{32.2}(10.72)^2 + \frac{1}{2}\frac{50}{32.2}(5.28)^2 = 57.4 \text{ ft-lb.}$$

The loss in kinetic energy is $89.4 - 57.4 = 32.0$ ft-lb.

Problems

1. A 10-lb. body with a velocity of 20 ft. per sec. strikes a 30-lb. body at rest. If the coefficient of restitution is 0.5, compute the velocities after impact and the loss in kinetic energy.
Ans. −2.5 ft. per sec.; 7.5 ft. per sec.; 35.0 ft-lb.

2. With what velocity must a 12-lb. body strike a 10-lb. body at rest to give the latter a velocity of 50 ft. per sec. if the coefficient of restitution is 0.5?
Ans. 61.1 ft. per sec.

3. If the coefficient of restitution is 0.9, from what height must a ball be dropped upon a stationary slab if it is to rebound to a height of 20 ft.?
Ans. 24.7 ft.

4. A ball is thrown horizontally with an initial velocity of 100 ft. per sec. from a point 5 ft. above the ground and 70 ft. from a vertical wall. How high above the ground will the ball strike the wall if the coefficient of restitution is 0.8?
Ans. 1.72 ft.

5. The 30-lb. ball in Fig. 363 is released from rest in position *A* and allowed to strike the 40-lb. ball. If the coefficient of restitution is 0.6, to what angle θ with the vertical will the 40-lb. ball swing?
Ans. 30.4°.

FIG. 363. FIG. 364.

6. If the coefficient of restitution is 0.8, with what velocity must the 25-lb. body in Fig. 364 strike the 10-lb. body in order to cause it to swing through an arc of 90°?
Ans. 19.8 ft. per sec.

Art. 100. Angular Impulse and Momentum; Plane Motion.
The *angular impulse* of a force F with respect to a given axis is
the moment of its linear impulse. Thus, if a constant force F at
distance r from an axis acts during time t, the linear impulse of the
force is Ft and the moment of this linear impulse is

$$\text{Angular impulse} = \mathbf{F\,t\,r} \approx ML^2T^{-1}$$

If the force is variable, the angular impulse may be taken for a
differential interval dt and then integrated to obtain the total
angular impulse, $\int Fr\,dt$. The unit of angular impulse is the
foot-pound-second.

The *angular momentum* of a particle with respect to a given
axis is the moment of its linear momentum. The angular momentum of a rotating body is the
summation of the moments of
momentum of all particles in
the body. Thus, in Fig. 365,
dM is the mass of any particle
at distance ρ from the axis O
about which the body is rotating with angular velocity ω.
The tangential velocity of the
particle is $\rho\omega$ and its linear
momentum is $dM\rho\omega$ as indi-

Fig. 365.

cated. The moment of momentum of the particle is $dM\rho^2\omega$.
The summation of these elementary moments of momentum for
the entire body is the angular momentum of the body.

$$\int dM\rho^2\omega = \omega \int \rho^2 dM = I_0\omega$$

Angular Momentum $= \mathbf{I_0\omega} \approx ML^2T^{-1}$

Since the dimensions of angular momentum are the same as for
angular impulse, the same unit, the foot-pound-second, is used
for each.

The relation between the angular impulse of the forces acting
on a rotating body and the change of angular momentum is
obtained from the equation $Fr = I\alpha$ (Art. 80). Let both sides of
this equation be multiplied by dt.

$$Fr\,dt = I\alpha dt$$

Since $\alpha = d\omega/dt$ by definition, the equation becomes,

$$Fr\, dt = I\, d\omega$$

The above equation may now be integrated between limits 0 and t for time and ω_0 and ω for angular velocity.

$$\int_0^t Fr\, dt = I \int_{\omega_0}^\omega d\omega = I\omega - I\omega_0$$

If the force F is constant, the above equation becomes

$$\mathbf{F\, t\, r = I\omega - I\omega_0}$$

It is thus seen that the angular impulse received by a rotating body is equal to the change in angular momentum of the body. This principle may be applied to advantage in the solution of problems in rotation involving force, time, and angular velocity.

Angular impulse and angular momentum are both vector quantities and may be resolved into components or combined into resultants as desired. The vector, representing graphically either angular impulse or angular momentum, is parallel to the axis of rotation and so directed that, if the rotation appears clockwise to an observer looking along the axis, the vector points away. For the counterclockwise rotation shown in Fig. 365, the vectors would be perpendicular to the plane of the figure and toward the observer. This convention may be described as the right-hand screw rule, since the direction of the vector bears the same relation to the direction of rotation as the advance of a right-hand screw to its direction of rotation.

Impulse and momentum methods are also applicable in the analysis of problems in plane motion. As explained in Art. 94, any plane motion may be considered as a motion of rotation, about an axis through the center of gravity of the body, combined with a linear motion of translation of the center of gravity. The equation $Ft = Mv - Mv_0$ is then applied to the motion of translation, and the equation $Ftr = I\omega - I\omega_0$ is applied to the motion of rotation. In the latter case, both angular impulse and angular momentum must be taken with respect to the axis through the center of gravity.

Example 1

A 50-lb. body is suspended from a cable which wraps around a 100-lb. cylinder 3 ft. in diameter and free to rotate about its geometric axis as shown in Fig. 366.   If the system is released from rest, determine the angular velocity of the cylinder at the end of 2 sec., and the tension in the cable.

FIG. 366.   FIG. 367:

Solution: The system is separated into two parts, one having motion of rotation as shown in Fig. 367 (*a*), and the other having motion of translation as shown in Fig. 367 (*b*).   The unknown cable tension is represented by T.   The linear impulse of this force is $T \times t = 2T$, and is represented as a vector in the figure.

A procedure involving the use of a principle similar to the D'Alembert principle (Art. 62) is of advantage in many problems of impulse and momentum.   The procedure consists of applying the momentum of the body in the reversed direction and then considering the impulse and the reversed momentum as a system in equilibrium.   Accordingly, the momentum Mv of the 50-lb. body is shown reversed in direction in Fig. 367 (*b*). The vector representing the angular momentum $I_0\omega$ of the rotating part is actually normal to the plane of the figure and parallel to the axis of rotation and thus would not appear in the figure.   In order to indicate the direction of the reversed angular momentum, the dotted arrow is used.

The moment of inertia of the cylinder is

$$I_0 = \frac{1}{2}\frac{100}{32.2}\,(1.5)^2 = 3.50$$

The angular impulse for the cylinder is $T \times 2 \times 1.5$.

$$T \times 2 \times 1.5 - 3.5\omega = 0 \qquad (1)$$

For the 50-lb. body,

$$T \times 2 + \frac{50}{32.2} \times v - 50 \times 2 = 0 \qquad (2)$$

also,

$$v = r\omega = 1.5\omega \qquad (3)$$

Simultaneous solution of equations (1), (2), and (3) gives,

$$T = 25 \text{ lb.}; \quad \omega = 21.4 \text{ rad. per sec.} = 204 \text{ r.p.m.}$$

An alternative solution by means of which ω may be determined in a single step consists of taking the two parts together as a single system, as shown in Fig. 368.   By moments about O,

$$50 \times 2 \times 1.5 - \frac{50}{32.2} \times v \times 1.5 - 3.5\omega = 0$$

By substitution of $v = r\omega = 1.5\omega$ and solving,

$$\omega = 21.4 \text{ rad. per sec.} = 204 \text{ r.p.m.}$$

The cable tension T may now be determined by considering the 50-lb. body alone.

Fig. 368.

Example 2

A solid sphere starts from rest and rolls freely down a 30° inclined plane.   Compute the linear velocity of the center of the sphere at the end of 2 sec.

Solution: Let the weight of the sphere be represented by W, the radius by r, and the static friction preventing slipping by F.   The moment of inertia of the sphere with respect to an axis through its center of gravity is $I_C = \frac{2}{5}\frac{W}{g}r^2$.

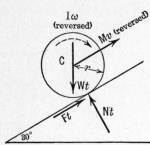

Fig. 369.

This is an example of plane motion and may be solved by considering the motion as one of rotation about the center of gravity C, combined with translation of C.   The reversed linear momentum Mv and the reversed angular momentum $I_C\omega$ are in the directions indicated in Fig. 369.   The various external impulses are also shown.   By summation parallel to the incline,

$$(W \times 2) \sin 30° - F \times 2 - \frac{W}{32.2} v = 0 \qquad (1)$$

By summation of moments about C,

$$(F \times 2) \times r - \frac{2}{5}\frac{W}{32.2} r^2 \cdot \omega = 0 \tag{2}$$

Also

$$v = r\omega \tag{3}$$

Simultaneous solution of equations (1), (2), and (3) gives

$$v = 23.0 \text{ ft. per sec.}$$

Problems

1. A 1200-lb. flywheel with a radius of gyration of 1.75 ft. is keyed to a 4-in. diameter shaft which turns in bearings for which the coefficient of friction is 0.05. If the power is cut off when the wheel is rotating at 300 r.p.m., how long will it take to come to rest under the action of friction alone?
Ans. 5 min. 58 sec.

2. A cylinder 4 ft. in diameter starts up a 15° incline with an angular velocity of 90 r.p.m. If no slipping occurs, how long will it continue to move up the slope?
Ans. 3.39 sec.

Fig. 370.

3. The roller in Fig. 370 weighs 200 lb. and has a radius of gyration of 5 in. If the system starts from rest and no slipping occurs, what will be the angular velocity of the roller at the end of 3 sec.?
Ans. 103 r.p.m.

4. Solve Prob. 3 if the cable is wrapped around the roller and comes off the top in a horizontal direction toward the pulley.   *Ans.* 176 r.p.m.

Art. 101. Conservation of Angular Momentum. If mutual interaction takes place between rotating bodies or parts of the same rotating body the action and reaction exerted between any pair are equal and opposite. If no external angular impulse is applied to the system during this time, the resultant angular impulse is zero and there will be no change in the angular momentum of the system. For instance, let the two wheels shown in Fig. 371 rotate independently of each other about the same axis

Fig. 371.

with angular velocities ω_1 and ω_2. If by means of a clutch or other device the wheels are now connected, the angular velocity of each is changed, but the total angular momentum of the system must remain constant, since no external angular impulse has been applied. Thus, if the new angular velocities are ω_1' and ω_2',

$$I_1\omega_1 + I_2\omega_2 = I_1\omega_1' + I_2\omega_2'$$

If no separation occurs after the wheels are connected, the final angular velocities ω_1' and ω_2' are identical and the above relation becomes

$$I_1\omega_1 + I_2\omega_2 = (I_1 + I_2)\omega$$

Problems

1. Two pulleys similar in all respects to each other are rotating in opposite directions on the same shaft with angular velocities of 30 r.p.m. and 60 r.p.m. If the two pulleys are suddenly connected by means of a clutch, what will be their common angular velocity?   *Ans.* 15 r.p.m.

2. In Fig. 371, wheel 1 is a solid cylinder of 2-ft. diameter and weighing 150 lb.; wheel 2 is a solid cylinder of 1.5-ft. diameter and weighing 80 lb. Wheel 1 is rotating at 120 r.p.m. and wheel 2 is at rest. If the two wheels are suddenly connected and forced to rotate together, determine the resulting angular velocity and the loss in kinetic energy. *Ans.* 92.4 r.p.m.; 42.2 ft-lb.

Art. 102. Impact of Translating Body with Rotating Body.

In Fig. 372 is shown a body of mass M_1 and weight W_1 which has linear velocity v_1, just before direct impact with a body of mass M_2 and weight W_2, which has angular velocity ω_2 about a fixed horizontal axis through O. The linear momentum of the mass M_1 before impact is M_1v_1; the angular momentum of M_1 with respect to the axis through O is the moment of the linear momentum and is thus M_1v_1r. The angular momentum of the rotating body is $I_2\omega_2$. Thus the total angular momentum of the system before impact is $M_1v_1r + I_2\omega_2$.

Fig. 372.

If the linear velocity of M_1 after impact is v_1' and the angular velocity of M_2 is ω_2', then the total angular momentum of the system after impact is $M_1v_1'r + I_2\omega_2'$.

During impact, the two bodies act on each other with equal and opposite forces; hence the angular impulses received are equal and opposite. The resultant angular impulse is thus zero, and there can be no change in angular momentum of the system. The total momentum of the system before impact may then be equated to the total momentum after impact.

$$M_1 v_1 r + I_2 \omega_2 = M_1 v_1' r + I_2 \omega_2' \tag{1}$$

If the two bodies do not separate after impact, the above equation alone is sufficient to determine the velocity after impact. If separation occurs, a second equation involving the coefficient of restitution may be used. From Art. 99,

$$v_2' - v_1' = e(v_1 - v_2)$$

Since $v_2' = r\omega_2'$ and $v_2 = r\omega_2$, the above equation becomes

$$r\omega_2' - v_1' = e(v_1 - r\omega_2) \tag{2}$$

Equations (1) and (2) together are now sufficient to determine the velocities after impact.

Example

In Fig. 372, let $W_1 = 0.1$ lb. be the weight of a bullet fired with a velocity of 1600 ft. per sec. directly at the center of percussion Q of a timber 6 ft. long of uniform cross section whose weight W_2 is 40 lb., and which is hanging at rest from a horizontal axis O at the upper end. If the bullet remains embedded in the wood, determine the angular velocity of the timber just after the impact.

Solution: The timber may, with very little error, be considered as a slender rod.

$$I_0 = \frac{1}{3}\frac{W}{g} l^2 = \frac{1}{3}\frac{40}{32.2}(6)^2 = 14.9$$

The distance r from O to the center of percussion is

$$r = \frac{k_0^2}{\bar{r}} = \frac{\frac{1}{3}l^2}{l/2} = \tfrac{2}{3}l = 4 \text{ ft.}$$

Substituting in eq. (1),

$$\frac{0.1}{32.2} \times 1600 \times 4 + 14.9 \times 0 = \frac{0.1}{32.2} \times 4\omega_2' \times 4 + 14.9\omega_2'$$

$$\omega_2' = 1.33 \text{ rad. per sec.}$$

Problems

1. Fig. 373 shows a cylinder of 1.5-ft. diameter and weighing 150 lb. from which is suspended a 50-lb. block. If the block is lifted upwards a distance of 2 ft. and then dropped, compute the angular velocity of the cylinder immediately after the cable becomes taut. *Ans.* 57.7 r.p.m.

2. If the timber described in the example above swings 30° from the vertical, compute the velocity of the bullet before impact. *Ans.* 1770 ft. per sec.

Fig. 373.

Art. 103. Gyroscopic Action.

Any rotating body is found to resist a change in the direction of its axis of rotation, the effect being particularly noticeable in bodies having relatively large moments of inertia or high speed of rotation. This effect, called *gyroscopic action*, is utilized in such devices as gyroscopic stabilizers, the gyroscopic compass, and gyroscopic steering mechanisms. A complete discussion of gyroscopic action is beyond the scope of this book, and this article will be limited to a consideration of gyroscopic action where the spin axis, torque axis, and precession axis are mutually rectangular.

(a)

(b)

Fig. 374.

The principles of angular impulse and momentum may be used in the analysis of gyroscopic motion. In Fig. 374 (a) is shown a wheel rotating with angular velocity ω about the horizontal axis AB, henceforth known as the spin axis. The angular momentum of the wheel is $I\omega$ which may be represented by a vector parallel to the axis of rotation as explained in Art. 100, the direction of the vector being from A toward B according to the right-hand screw rule. The angular momentum about the spin axis is thus represented by the vector OM in Fig. 374 (b). Now let a torque T be applied, tending to rotate the body and spin axis about the z axis in the clockwise direction. During a differential time dt, the angular impulse is $T\,dt$, which produces an equal change in angular momentum, represented by the vector ON. The resultant of the two angular momentum vectors is OP, at angle $d\phi$ with the original direction of the spin axis. The spin axis thus must rotate about the y axis to the new position OP. As long as the torque continues to act the spin axis continues to rotate. This rotation of the spin axis is called *precession*. Thus, whenever a torque about an axis normal to the spin axis is applied to a rotating body, the body will not rotate about the torque axis but will rotate or precess about a third axis normal to the two.

The angular velocity of precession will now be determined. From Fig. 374 (b),

$$ON = OM \cdot d\phi$$

$$T\,dt = I\omega \cdot d\phi$$

$$T = I\omega\,\frac{d\phi}{dt}$$

The quantity $d\phi/dt$, is the rate of change of the angular position of the spin axis and is thus the angular velocity of precession, denoted by Ω. Hence,

$$\mathbf{T} = \mathbf{I\omega\Omega}$$

As long as the torque and the angular velocity of spin remain unchanged, the velocity of precession will be constant.

A forced precession about an axis perpendicular to the spin axis causes a torque about a third rectangular axis. Thus the wheels of a car going around a curve are forced to precess about a vertical axis through the center of the curve. A torque is thereby produced about an axis tangent to the curve making the road pressure on the outer wheels more and on the inner wheels less than it would be on a straight road. This effect is in addition to that produced by centrifugal action.

Example

A car rounds a curve of 200 ft. radius at 40 mi. per hr. Each wheel and tire has outside diameter of 2 ft., weighs 50 lb., and has radius of gyration of 10 in.   Determine the additional road pressure on an outside wheel due to gyroscopic action if the tread is 5 ft.

FIG. 375.

Solution: In Fig. 375, a pair of wheels and connecting axle is shown as the car recedes from the observer.   For the two wheels,

$$I = \frac{W}{g} k^2 = \frac{100}{32.2} \left(\frac{10}{12}\right)^2 = 2.16$$

$v = 40$ mi. per hr. $= 58.7$ ft. per sec.

$\omega = v/r' = 58.7/1 = 58.7$ rad. per sec.

$\Omega = v/r = 58.7/200 = 0.294$ rad. per sec.

The vector representing the angular momentum $I\omega$ about the spin axis is shown in the figure. The forced precession takes place about the y axis as indicated. The corresponding change in angular momentum must be produced by an equal angular impulse $T\,dt$ in the z direction as shown. The torque T required to produce the angular impulse is given by $T = I\omega\Omega$. The torque is due to an increased pressure R_o on the outer wheel and an equally decreased pressure R_i on the inner wheel and is therefore $R_o \times 5$.   Hence,

$$T = R_o \times 5 = I\omega\Omega$$

$$R_o = \frac{2.16 \times 58.7 \times 0.294}{5} = 7.46 \text{ lb.}$$

Problems

1. Determine the gyroscopic effect on a side-wheel steamer when it makes a sharp turn to the left.   *Ans.* Left side is tilted upward.

2. Determine the gyroscopic effect on a ship with a screw propeller when a wave strikes it from the front tending to lift the bow. Assume that the rotation of the propeller is clockwise when viewed from behind.

Ans. Ship turns to the right.

3. Solve the Example on page 261 if the velocity of the car is increased to 60 mi. per hr.   *Ans.* 16.7 lb.

4. The wheel of a gyroscope weighs 40 lb. and has a radius of gyration of 2 ft.   The wheel spins at 300 r.p.m. about a horizontal axle supported on a pivot 3 ft. along the axle from the wheel.   Determine the velocity of precession due to the gravity torque.   *Ans.* 7.35 r.p.m.

5. Show that an airplane, with the propeller and engine rotating clockwise as viewed from the rear, can be turned to the right by elevating a horizontal rudder at the stern.

Supplementary Problems

1. A cylindrical stream of water 3 in. in diameter with a velocity of 50 ft. per sec. impinges normally upon a flat vane moving with velocity of 20 ft. per sec. in the same direction as the water.   Compute the force exerted on the vane and the horsepower developed by the vane.   *Ans.* 85.7 lb.; 3.12 hp.

2. If the stream of water described in Prob. 1 impinges tangentially upon a stationary curved vane which changes the direction of the water by 180°, compute the resultant force exerted on the vane.   *Ans.* 477 lb.

3. A stream of water impinges normally upon a flat vane moving in the same direction as the water.   Show that the vane develops maximum power when its velocity is one-third the velocity of the stream of water.   (Suggestion: Develop the expression for the power in terms of the area of the stream, its velocity, the density of water, and the velocity of the vane.   Then apply the customary mathematical procedure for determining a maximum.)

4. The hammer of a pile driver descends vertically between fixed guides. If the weight of the hammer is 2000 lb. and the friction of the guides is 150 lb., how long will it take the hammer, starting from rest, to acquire a velocity of 75 ft. per sec.?   The hammer, after striking, is drawn back up with a velocity of 10 ft. per sec.   If this velocity is to be acquired in 2 sec., what cable pull is needed?   *Ans.* 2.52 sec.; 2460 lb.

5. A 750-lb. projectile is fired with a muzzle velocity of 1800 ft. per sec. from a gun weighing 150,000 lb.   Neglecting the reaction due to the discharged gases, what must be the scale of a set of springs to limit the recoil of the gun to a distance of 3 ft.?   *Ans.* 3500 lb. per in.

6. A bullet weighing $\frac{1}{2}$ oz. and moving horizontally with a velocity of 2000 ft. per sec. strikes centrally a block of wood weighing 10 lb. which is suspended by a cord from a point 3 ft. above the center of the block.   To what angle from the vertical will the block and embedded bullet swing?

Ans. 37.0°.

7. A ball is dropped from a height of 20 ft. upon a stationary slab. If the coefficient of restitution is 0.4, how high will the ball rebound? *Ans.* 3.2 ft.

8. If a ball is dropped from a height of h feet upon a stationary slab and rebounds to a height of h' feet, show that the coefficient of restitution is given by $e = \sqrt{h'/h}$.

9. A body weighing 80 lb. and having a velocity of 5 ft. per sec. to the left collides with a second body weighing 100 lb. and having a velocity of 10 ft. per sec. to the right. The coefficient of restitution is 0.5. Determine the velocity of each body after impact and the loss in kinetic energy for the system.
Ans. 7.5 ft. per sec. to the right; zero; 117 ft-lb.

10. The rotating parts of the windlass shown in Fig. 376 weigh 120 lb. and have a radius of gyration of 1 ft. The 400-lb. body is falling with a velocity of 20 ft. per sec. just before the brake is applied. If the coefficient of friction for the brake is 0.5 and friction at the bearing is neglected, in what time will the brake bring the system to rest when applied with a force $N = 400$ lb.? Determine the tension in the cable while the brake is acting.
Ans. 5.46 sec.; 445 lb.

11. A sphere of 1.5-ft. diameter and weighing 80 lb. starts from rest and rolls down a 30° inclined plane without slipping. Determine the friction at the surface required to prevent slipping and the linear velocity of the sphere after 10 sec.
Ans. 11.4 lb.; 115 ft. per sec.

FIG. 376.

12. Two cast-iron spheres 6 in. in diameter are mounted on a slender rod with their centers 2 ft. apart. The system rotates at a speed of 30 r.p.m. in a horizontal plane about a vertical axis through the middle of the rod. If, by means of a spring, the spheres are brought into contact at the center, determine the new speed of rotation. *Ans.* 352 r.p.m.

13. A pair of drive wheels and connecting axle of a locomotive have weight of 4000 lb., a diameter of 64 in., and a radius of gyration of 20 in. Determine the added pressure on the outer wheel due to gyroscopic action when the locomotive rounds a curve of 1000-ft. radius at a speed of 60 mi. per hr. The distance between centers of rails is 4.9 ft. *Ans.* 205 lb.

14. A rotary airplane engine having weight of 325 lb. and radius of gyration of 14 in. makes 1300 r.p.m. when the plane has a speed of 150 mi. per hr. Compute the gyroscopic torque exerted on the plane when making a turn of 200-ft. radius. If the distance from the center of pressure of the tail to the center of gravity of the plane is 15 ft., compute the force acting on the tail.
Ans. 2060 ft-lb.; 137 lb.

INDEX